The Making of
SCOTTISH
GEOGRAPHY

100 YEARS OF THE R.S.G.S.

I. H. ADAMS
A. J. CROSBIE
G. GORDON

Department of Geography, University of Edinburgh,
and the
Royal Scottish Geographical Society

EDINBURGH
1984

CONTENTS

LIST OF ILLUSTRATIONS

PREFACE

The making of Scottish geography during the last hundred years has been the work of many individuals. This brief review summarising their contributions not only illustrates the progress of ideas and knowledge about Scotland during the period but also indicates the need for new appraisals in the rapidly changing world of today. The Royal Scottish Geographical Society was founded in response to the flourishing interest in geography generally, and that in Scotland particularly, in 1884, since when it has acted as a stimulus to, and provided support for, research and studies in the discipline. The journal of the Society, the **Scottish Geographical Magazine** has been the outlet for many of the resulting publications and has been used extensively in this summary. The familiar shorthand of the **S.G.M.** has been used throughout in referring to these in place of the standard abbreviation for the journal which is **Scott. Geogr. Mag.**.

Inevitably, a high degree of selectivity was required in compiling this account. In the early period there were few lines of demarcation between disciplines, many of which stemmed from the root of natural philosophy, and knowledge about Scotland grew through many channels. Later, a remarkably small, but extremely productive, number of professional geographers in the country up to the second World War consolidated the pattern which had been established and laid the foundations for the growth and diversity of interest which have marked the past three decades. During this recent period, many individual geographers have followed a highly specialised field of interest and there has also been a substantial overlap with other disciplines as the ecological perspective, so typical of the early years of the Society, has, once again, ascended.

The aim of this book is to present a holistic view of the geography of Scotland with an emphasis on publications by geographers in the S.G.M. It marks the centenary of the R.S.G.S., but we hope that it will be relevant and useful to all involved in appreciating, and stimulating an understanding of, the Scottish people and environment.

Edinburgh,
October, 1984

I. H. Adams
A. J. Crosbie
G. Gordon

ACKNOWLEDGEMENTS

This publication was prepared at short notice and it would not have been possible without the assistance and willing co-operation of members of the Department of Geography, University of Edinburgh. In particular, we acknowledge with gratitude the skill of Steve Dowers in setting the text, Morag Innes in designing the cover, Ray Harris, David Lennie and Douglas Hunter in printing, and Norma Dunn in preparing the illustrations from various sources. George Outram and Company gave permission for the use of photographs from the Glasgow Herald in Figure 9.

1. THE FORMATIVE YEARS

Just like today, Scotland in the period when the Royal Scottish Geographical Society was formed at the end of the nineteenth century was a country undergoing great changes. New horizons brought about by exploration, discovery and greatly improved communications gave rise to new outlooks, new environments due to urbanisation and industrialisation demanded continual adaptation, and new ideas in science and philosophy stimulated curiosity and intellectual excitement. 1884 was itself an unusual year with brilliant sunsets persisting after the great explosion of Krakatoa in 1883, the Royal Society of Edinburgh celebrating its centenary, and the congregation of many famous men including Ferdinand de Lessops, the builder of the Suez Canal, for the tercentenary of the University of Edinburgh. The British Empire was flourishing with Glasgow proud of being the Second City in it, while Africa, with its Scottish link in David Livingstone and its topical interest with the struggle for spheres of influence by the countries of Europe, became the focus of attention when the Society attracted H. M. Stanley to give the inaugural address.

The geography of Scotland, however, had been changing since the failure of the Old Pretender in "the Fifteen". This spurred on the mapping of Scotland but, more importantly, opened up a largely inaccessible land through the roads and bridges of General Wade. In turn, these were improved by Macadam and the greatest of the civil engineers, Thomas Telford, who used the natural landforms as a guide for his routes and ensured that his roads harmonised with their surroundings. When, in time, the railways followed knowledge about the country accumulated outwards from them. The development of transport brought about diverse responses. On the one hand, the birth of a tourist industry was induced by the romantic novels of Walter Scott and Queen Victoria establishing a summer residence on Deeside ; on the other, it facilitated an exodus from the rural to the new urban areas and a growing flood of emigration to the colonies, particularly Canada, Australia and New Zealand.

"Such is the prevailing taste for scientific pursuits, that many Tourists now blend the love of Natural Scenery with a devotion to Natural Science ; for such, numerous notices of the Geology, Botany, and Natural History, of the various districts have been interspersed throughout this Edition ; and a Geological map, pointing out the leading formations, will be found among the illustrations".

So stated the preface to **Lizars' Scottish Tourist** in 1850 when 18,000 copies had already been sold, but understanding the evolution of the physical landscape required more than an appreciation of the processes involved. There was still in the first half of the nineteenth century a belief in 'The Flood' or a diluvian cause for the natural features of the country. In 1857, Hugh Miller, whose name is forever linked with the Old Red Sandstone of Northeast Scotland, (1857) illustrated and bridged the gap between the past and the scientific outlook of the latter nineteenth century in his classic book **The Testimony of the Rocks : Geology in its bearing on the two theologies, natural and revealed.**

The release of mental constraints produced a burst of activity, first in the brief but scintillating period of the Scottish Enlightenment but then in sustained and flourishing scientific endeavour. Roderick Murchison, a Ross-shire Highlander, was the leading geologist of the mid nineteenth century and endowed the Chair of Geology at Edinburgh in 1871 with the stipulation that Archibald Geikie be the first incumbent. The **Scenery of Scotland** by Geikie (1865) was the first attempt to elucidate in some detail the history of the topography of a country, and the principles used had universal significance. It laid out the basic divisions of Scotland, introduced the terms Southern Uplands and Central Lowlands for the first time, and illustrated the belief of the Edinburgh School of Geologists who maintained the importance of denudation in the shaping of the landscape. When the Scottish branch of the Geological Survey was established in 1867, Geikie was the first Director and he held this post concurrently with his appointment at the University until he moved to London in 1881. He regarded himself as a physical geographer and his blend of structural and applied geology was sustained when he was succeeded at Edinburgh University by his brother, James Geikie.

The Challenger expedition had a major impact on Scottish scientific life. After completing the greatest investigation of the oceans to date in 1876, the 50 volumes of the report were edited in Edinburgh firstly by Wyville Thomson and then by John Murray. The influence of Murray on the last two decades of the nineteenth century in Edinburgh was immense. He was born in Canada and educated in Scotland although his reputation must be the envy of every student in its claim that he took every class in the University of Edinburgh but never an examination (Mill, 1934). As a junior naturalist on the Challenger in 1872, he made his mark and in his role as Director and Editor he stimulated all aspects of the natural sciences. The expedition provided a bench mark against which other developments could be evaluated and, in consequence, there was a steady stream of reports, specimens and distinguished scientists coming to Edinburgh. The meteorological observations taken on the Challenger expedition were analysed for global isothermal and isobaric maps by Alexander Buchan. Originally a schoolmaster, Buchan became the leading

Figure 1: John Murray

meteorologist in Great Britain and, as Secretary of the Scottish
Meteorological Society, was the driving force in establishing the
Observatory on the summit of Ben Nevis in 1884. A direct
consequence of the interest in the oceans was the establishment
of the Scottish Marine Station at Granton in 1883 soon to be
followed by another at Millport on the Clyde.

Natural history increased in popularity throughout the
nineteenth century, particularly after Darwin published the
Origin of Species. Unlike England where the emphasis was on the
attributes of the individual species, the interest in Scotland
was on interrelationships in local environments and the role of
geographical isolation in species development. J. Arthur Thomson
and Patrick Geddes succeeded Huxley in giving a geographical
pespective to the biological sciences. Complexity and variety
were the key factors, both of which are evident and significant
in Scotland where the rigours of the latitude, although
ameliorated by a favourable climate, stress differences due to
aspect or altitude.

The invigorating scientific climate of the time was,
however, only one aspect of Scottish affairs. Political
stability after the '45 resulted in immense changes in the human
geography of Scotland. Edinburgh, with the energy of its
population confined within the multi-storey tenements on the
ridge of the Old Town for centuries, exploded its boundaries to
the north in the New Town and to the south beyond the Meadows.
In the Victorian era the expansion of stone tenements to provide
housing adjacent to factories and transport facilities was a
feature of all Scottish cities. The economic balance of the
country shifted from the predominantly agricultural east to the
growing industrial conurbation in the Clyde valley. John
Sinclair, who introduced the new methods of agriculture which
made the Lothians and the carse lands of the east coast the best
farmed land in Britain, organised and compiled the **Statistical
Account of Scotland** which not only gives a full description of
Scotland in the last decade of the eighteenth century but also
provides a bench mark for measuring subsequent change.
Nationalism was a flame in Europe and some of the heat was
evident in Scotland with a growing demand for the preservation of
Scottish traditions and a degree of political autonomy (Adams,
1984). Lord Rosebery was the key figure in the cause for a
Scottish dimension, both in government and higher education. The
role of geography in administration, whether within Great Britain
or in the wider context of the Empire, was increasingly apparent.
It is not surprising, therefore, that the Royal Scottish
Geographical Society and the Scottish Office were founded almost
simultaneously, that Lord Rosebery was the first President of the
Society having recently resigned as the first under-secretary of
state at the Home Office responsible for Scottish affairs, and
that the Society was, from the beginning, a prestigious

Figure 2: James Geikie

organisation. It was also, however, a society conceived and initiated with widespread popular support as branches were inaugurated, again addressed by H. M. Stanley, at Dundee and Glasgow immediately after the "grand launching ceremony" on 3rd. December, 1984. A branch was formed in Aberdeen early in 1885.

The role of the Scottish Geographical Magazine in making the geography of Scotland has been very important. The publication of a journal was an integral part of the original scheme for, without it, the Sociey would only have had local importance. It was intended as a means of contact with geographers and other societies throughout the world and as a channel for summarising the progress of geographical knowledge and bringing its readers into touch with the general scientific world. The first monthly issue appeared in February, 1885, and it has been published continuously ever since. For Scotland, it not only provided a window on the globe but also presented an outlet for the accumulation of papers on all aspects of Scottish geography which otherwise would have been scattered, and limited, in diverse journals. Editors are critically important in ensuring the success of a journal and the R.S.G.S. has been fortunate in this regard, particularly from 1902-34 when Marion Newbigin shaped both the S.G.M. and much of British geography.

The pre-eminence of Scotland in science at the end of the nineteenth century was partly due to coincidence as events drew world attention to Edinburgh and there was a concentration of influential figures working in the country (Lochhead, 1984).It was also due to the attitude towards geography and education which prevailed at the time. The importance of geography was well recognised and, as an example, it was one of the founding subjects listed in the charter for Edinburgh University. In the eighteenth century there was renewed interest, particularly in the practical aspects required for navigation, and in the nineteenth century this developed within the growing education system. Academic geography, however, was non-existent and the making of Scottish geography at this time was the work of engineers, surveyors, naturalists and individuals in other disciplines. The names of those who established geography belong to people who were originally trained in different subjects. In itself, this is an indicator of the vitality and fascination of the discipline as men like H. N. Dickson, A. J. Herbertson, W. S. Bruce and H. R. Mill brought their training in the sciences at Edinburgh to bear, and George C. Chisholm moved from literary work for a Glasgow publisher to his vocation as geographer. Small wonder that Scotland was, in Elspeth Lochhead's words "the cradle of modern academic geography in Britain" (1981).

2. THE ENVIRONMENTAL SETTING

The tradition of expertise in the natural and field sciences was well established in Scotland when the R.S.G.S. was inaugurated. This, combined with the scientific background of many of the founding figures of the Society, the interdisciplinary approach in natural history and the interest in the features and characteristics of newly explored lands provided the essential foundations on which knowledge of the Scottish environment has been built throughout the past century. The Geological Survey was well established and detailed and comprehensive accounts of various parts of the country have been published in its Geological Memoirs. A holistic view of this basic core to the environment has constantly developed and is effectively expressed in **Geology of Scotland** edited by Craig (1965, 1983).

The spectacular scenery of Scotland is strongly correlated with the underlying rocks, but the concept of changing scenery due to erosion was first formulated by James Hutton at the end of the eighteenth century. While he appreciated the effect of glaciation in Switzerland, he did not perceive the same history in Scotland. It was the Swiss geologist, Louis Agassiz, who visited Scotland in 1840 (Davies, 1968) and confirmed the effects of glaciation (1840) in the striated surface of the "cave" at Blackford Hill, Edinburgh. He argued that a great ice sheet had covered Scotland and that glacier ice had blocked the former lakes of Glen Roy to produce the famous "parallel roads". Initially, there was resistance to this view but in 1863 Archibald Geikie presented widespread evidence of former ice-sheets and glaciers and general acceptance rapidly followed. By 1894, when the third edition of James Geikie's **Great Ice Age** was published, "Scotland led the world in this field of study and the essential foundations of our more detailed knowledge of today had been firmly laid" (Sissons, 1967).

From that time, the geomorphology of Scotland has been thoroughly studied, both in general and in detail. The **Story of the Forth** by H. M. Cadell (191) was an early example. Cadell, who began as a professional geologist, had to move into the family engineering business but retained his interest and carried out comprehensive studies of West Lothian. He played a prominent part in the R.S.G.S. and published many papers in the S.G.M. Like many of the early geographers, his interests were widespread and he ranged from industrial development (1904) to the Stirling coalfield (1933). Others followed but the most significant contribution came from David Linton. As a lecturer at Edinburgh in the 1930s, Linton carried out field work in many parts of Scotland and elucidated the processes involved in drainage evolution and in glaciation (1934, 1949, 1951).

In the spirit and stature of the great pioneers, Brian Sissons inspired a school of postgraduate geomorphologists at Edinburgh in a series of detailed, meticulous studies of the Scottish landscape. **The evolution of Scotland's scenery** follows in the classic tradition of Geikie and provides a benchmark in Quaternary geomorphology (Sissons,1967). His research produced an extensive series of publications beginning with the deglaciation of East Lothian (1958) and continuing with more than fifty books, contributions and papers, many of them in the S.G.M. (see references). He inspired a large, devoted group of postgraduates, many of whom now hold university positions, and they, in turn, added to the knowledge of Scotland. At Glasgow, R. B. Price drew together much of the material on Highland landforms (1974) and the evolution of Scotland's environment (1983), Colin Ballantyne at St. Andrews has illustrated the sequence of events in East Argyll (1979), Kirby the ground moraines of the Lothians (1968), and Cullingford and Smith described lateglacial shorelines in east Scotland. Gray and Lowe edited studies of the lateglacial renvironment in Scotland (1977) while Sutherland described some of the problems of dating glacial deposits (1980). These are only a few examples of a vast stream of publications which have flowed from this school of geomorphologists.

Quaternary studies in northeast Scotland have not been neglected (Gemmel, 1975) and the glaciated history of the Cairngorms has been compiled by Sugden (1968,1969,1970) and Clapperton (1975). **The coastline of Scotland** by J. A. Steers (1973) provided a comprehensive review but more detailed studies of coastal morphology and the beaches of the north of Scotland have been carried out by Professor W. Ritchie and his colleagues at Abedeen (1966, 1967, 1968, 1969, 1970).

The climate, from the glacial periods of the past to the changing sequence of the present, has provided the mechanism for geomorphological variations. Study of Pleistocene climates has continued through the period beginning with James Geikie (1892) but the previous view that they consisted of four, or at the most six, major glacials has been replaced by the realisation that there were many more and, indeed, some seventeen glacials during the entire Quaternary . Historically, Edinburgh has one of the longest meteorological records in the world and early recognition of the effect of climate on health led to these being discussed in detail by Mossman (1895) and more recently by Plant (1968). The character and consequences of past climates, including the all too frequent famine (Walton, 1952), was reviewed by Taylor (1935). A great debt is due to H.R. Mill who established the British Rainfall Organisation. He trained as a chemist but abandoned it for geography in 1886. A keen and enthusiastic member of the R.S.G.S., he did much to extend its influence in his role as Convenor of the Corresponding Committee before he

Figure 3: Marion Newbigin

left to become Librarian of the Royal Geographical Society. The Scottish Meteorological Society did great pioneer work but the need for a synoptic view meant that a national organisation was essential. The Meteorological Office was established and has compiled climatological data for most areas of the country and published memoranda which are invaluable for planning and application purposes, e.g. Plant (1966). Other accounts, such as the description of the features of the Forth and Tay estuaries are rare (Gloyne, 1966). Moreover, the network of observation stations in Scotland is essentially on the lowlands (Halstead, 1956) although some high level stations have been established with the development of skiing in the Cairngorms. Much of the work carried out in Scotland, therefore, related to specific problems (Manley, 1945). Bioclimatic sub-regions (Birse, 1971), insolation (Garnett, 1939), fuel requirements (Manley, 1957), urban areas (Hamilton, 1963), air pollution (Crosbie, 1968) and natural hazards such as floods (Baird and Lewis, 1958, Common, 1954,1956, Learmonth, 1949) are significant in a marginal climate where minor changes in seasonal features, duration or intensity are immediately felt. Today, many of these problems may be anticipated as meteorological monitoring by satellite has become standard with information constantly gathered at the University of Dundee.

The surface waters of Scotland were exhaustively surveyed and the results published in the early years of the S.G.M. by Pullar and Murray (1903-1908). From these foundations, the monitoring of water resource data has continued with the work of the various River Authorities. Hydrology has received increasing attention in assessing runoff and sedimentation (Ledger, 1980).

Among the parents of modern British, let alone Scottish, geography, Marion Newbigin holds an outstanding place for her work on biogeography and physical geography. She not only contributed to the knowledge of Scotland but also laid the foundations of scientific method on which all is built. Her early training as a biologist led to **Life by the seashore** in 1901, but this was succeeded by many books and articles extending over the range of geography. Today, her successors such as Professor Joy Tivy, bring a holistic view in assessing the organic resources of Scotland (1973) in line with the ecological approach long established in geography. Nor is our knowledge confined to the present as a small, but active, school of pollen analysts (Birks, Durno, Newey) have revealed the vegetative cover of the past from the evidence retained in the great bogs, e.g. Flanders Moss.

The vegetation of Scotland is rich (Burnett, 1964) but the trappings are, of course, constantly changing sometimes as part of a natural progression but more frequently as a result of man's activities. Today, the work of the Forestry Commission has

Figure 4: H. R. Mill and Alexander Buchan

altered the face of Scotland.   Features of this scale inevitably require large organisations in order to survey them and the work of the Soil Survey of Scotland, based on the Macauley Institute at Aberdeen, the Scottish Peat Survey of the Department of Agriculture and Fisheries, and the Nature Conservancy have all contributed to a lucid picture of our basic resources. A wider summary of the resource base was given by Elgood (1961) for the Scottish Council (Development and Indusry) and an overall review of the natural environment of Scotland was edited by Goodier (1974).

The Scottish environment is unique.   Warmed by the positive temperature anomaly for the latitude of the North Atlantic, distanced from the continental influence of Europe by the North Sea, Scotland has scenery shaped by the glaciations of the, geologically speaking, recent past and clothed in vegetation which is varied and shown to perfection by the low angle sunshine of the seasons.   Despite these benefits, however, it possesses a marginal climate in which altitude very rapidly creates the conditions of high latitudes with strong prevailing winds, and where a southerly aspect is important in ameliorating the seasonal low temperatures. Agriculture, which is basic to the Scottish economy, is particularly sensitive to any change, however slight, in the pattern and characteristics of the seasons.

Appreciation and awareness of the environment is greater today than ever before, not least due to the work of John Muir, the Scot from Dunbar who became father of national parks in the United States.   It provides the setting for much of Scotland's economy and for recreation, and the concern for its conservation is strong, widespread and politically significant.

3. SCOTLAND MAPPED

The mapping of Scotland, and the study of that process, has been one of the most vigorously pursued fields of Scottish geography in which the Royal Scottish Geographical Society has played a leading role. By the time the Society was founded, Scotland already had a long and important tradition of map making. Alexander Lindsay's rutter of James V's expedition to the Isles in the summer of 1540 marks the beginning of indigenous efforts to define the shape of Scotland (Adams and Fortune, 1980). It was as a result of this voyage that knowledge of the outline of Scotland became available in a presentable form and it is presumed that it was used by George Lily, an Englishman in Rome, for his map of Britain published in 1546. In the last decade of that century Timothy Pont undertook his great survey which appeared in Blaeu's "Atlas Novus Pars quinta Scotia et Hibernia" in 1654. This marked the end of the first phase of Scottish cartography. The story of Pont and the subsequent publication of his work has attracted the attention of several scholars. The first papers were by by C.G. Cash (1901, 1907) and were followed by E.S. Reid-Tait (1930), J.H.G. Lebon (1952), D.G. Moir and R.A. Skelton (1968), Jeffrey C. Stone (1968, 1970, 1973, 1979, 1983), B.R.S. Megaw (1969), I.A. Kinniburgh (1968) and A.M. Findlay (1978). Interest in another early cartographer, John Adair, is largely covered in a paper by Inglis (1918) and extended by Arthur H.W. Robinson's report on two unrecorded charts (1959).

Military surveyors have made their mark in Scotland. The making of large-scale maps of Scotland began in the unhappy years of the Anglo-Scottish War which lasted from 1543 to 1550. The ensuing intelligence activity brought English land surveyors to Scotland who recorded places - Galloway, east coast Lowlands, Edinburgh and the Border valleys - along the invasion routes. It was the Earl of Hertford's invasion in May, 1544, that led to the first plan of Edinburgh being drawn. The next group of military plans that generated scholarly interest were those made by General George Wade for his Military Roads in Scotland (Inglis 1923, Mathieson 1924). The '45 stimulated a lot of cartographic activity, most prominent being Roy's military survey which provides a unique insight into the landscape between 1747 and 1755 at the very beginning of a period of great change (Gardiner 1977). Roy's map enabled A.C. O'Dell to assess the extent of open-field and enclosed land, plantations and natural woodlands at a very early stage of the improvements (1953). The career of this remarkable surveyor whose map, produced with limited facilities and at little expense, led to the founding of the Ordnance Survey, was documented by R. Miller (1956), R.A. Skelton (1967), and Yolande O'Donoghue (1977). The National Library of

Scotland has purchased a complete set of coloured slides of these unpublished fine maps, the manuscripts of which are housed in the British Library in London.

Another cartographic source of great importance in understanding the creation of the Scottish landscape comprises the manuscript plans made by land surveyors mainly in the period 1750 to 1850 (Adams, 1976). Often called estate plans, their usefulness was first demonstrated by Arthur Geddes in his study of agrarian change in the Lowlands (1938). Under his supervision this theme was developed by Betty M.W. Third (1955 and 1957). The momentum was maintained when I. H. Adams was appointed an editor in the Scottish Record Office, H.M. General Register House, in Edinburgh, to prepare a list of plans in their hands. In 1964, the Register House Plan (RHP) collection consisted of just over 3000 items but in the next few years this multiplied to little short of 100,000 items (Adams 1966, 1970, 1974, Sinclair 1977). Interest spread throughout Scotland: the Department of Geography in Aberdeen listed the estate plans of the Duke of Atholl, I.H. Adams was appointed honorary map curator by the Marquis of Linlithgow at Hopetoun House and, in addition to putting the estate plans on exhibition, published a monograph on the mapping of the estate (1971a). The National Register of Archives (Scotland) expanded their activities to include estate plans, and these clarified the role of the land surveyor in the evolution of today's landscape (Adam 1958, Adams 1967, 1968, 1975a, 1975b, McArthur 1936). The detailed understanding possible is illustrated by the **Papers on Peter May Land Surveyor 1749-1793** (Adams 1979). Estate plans have become one of the most useful sources for studying the changing rural landscape and this is reflected in the work of H. Fairhurst (1964, 1968), J.H.G. Lebon (1946, 1952), H.A. Moisley (1961), and M. Storrie (1961).

The production of county maps gave rise to several surveyor/cartographers in the eighteenth century, the most notable of whom was John Ainslie, born in Jedburgh in 1745 (Adams 1973). He was the second son of a writer, and, somehow, he became apprenticed to Thomas Jefferys "geographer to the King" by 1765 for he worked on Jefferys' large map of Bedfordshire which was surveyed in that year. Ainslie returned home after Jefferys died in 1771. After making a map of his home town he set out to prepare large-scale county maps of Selkirk, Fife and Kinross, the Lothians, Wigtownshire, Angus, Renfrewshire and Kirkcudbright (Parry 1975a). He went on to produce accurate charts of both the East and West coasts of Scotland (Robinson 1958). The sum of these works was embodied in his nine sheet map of Scotland, the issue of which was a landmark in the improvement of the outline of Scotland. For the first time the Great Glen from Inverness to Fort William is shown as a straight line, and Skye, Mull and Islay are shown with some degree of accuracy. His cartographic

Figure 5: John George Barthomolew

activity encompassed every dimension of the changing scene. He surveyed estates, such as those of the Earl of Eglinton, at the point of enclosure; he worked with Robert Whitworth surveying the line of a canal from the Forth to the Clyde; and he made plans of Leith and Port Glasgow harbours (Kinniburgh, 1960).

Transmission of his skills to posterity preoccupied Ainslie in his later years. He seems to have gone to considerable lengths in educating one of his apprentices, William Bald, who went on to gain an international reputation for his cartographic skills (Storrie 1969). At the age of sixty-seven John Ainslie felt it necessary to set down on paper his accumulated experience. In his book **A Comprehensive Treatise on Land Surveying** he sets out, with the use of practical examples, the theory and practices of surveying and describes the various instruments used in his craft. The whole is dedicated to his friend John Rennie, the civil engineer.

The name Bartholomew is irradicably linked both with map-making and the Royal Scottish Geographical Society. The story begins with the Edinburgh School of Geographical Engravers whose origins can be traced back to Bernard Picart a Frenchman working in Amsterdam in the early eighteenth century. He passed his skills on to John Pine, a Londoner, who in turn passed them on to another Englishman, Richard Cooper. Cooper left his employer on receiving an inheritance to go and study art in Rome. There he met Alexander Guthrie who invited him to visit Edinburgh, which he did, and he was prevailed upon to settle there in his old profession of map engraving. To him must be given the title of founder of the "School of Map Engraving in Edinburgh." One of his major commissions was to engrave John Adair's maps (Inglis, 1918). Andrew Bell, the founder of the **Encyclopaedia Britannica,** had been one of his apprentices. In turn he passed his skills on to Daniel Lizars who made many fine maps and who apprenticed the first John Bartholomew to the map making trade. The high cartographic standards and the business integrity of the firm of Bartholomews led to their rise to international levels by the end of the nineteenth century. John George Bartholomew (1860-1920) played an important role in their progress. He was educated at the Royal High School and the University of Edinburgh but, contracting tuberculosis immediately after graduation, he embarked on a voyage to Melbourne in 1881. His experiences there and on the return voyage, including a stop at Cape Town, must have fired his enthusiasm for in 1884 he was one of the founding members of the Society and in the words of Sir Ludovic Grant the "chief architect of its prosperity".

John George Bartholomew was to draw together a group of the most distinguished men of the day who were interested in geography: the Geikie brothers, Sir George Adam Smith, Sir Patrick Geddes, George Chisholm, Ernest Shackleton, Cecil Rhodes,

H.M. Stanley and the oceanographer Sir John Murray. It was he who founded the Edinburgh Geographical Institute, first in Park Road and later in Duncan Street, Edinburgh. John George, as he is distinguished in the Bartholomew line, was awarded the Victoria Gold Medal of the Royal Geographical Society for his "successful efforts to raise the standards of cartography " (Gardiner 1976).

The Royal Scottish Geographical Society and John George Bartholomew collaborated to produce the **Survey Atlas of Scotland**. This was very advanced for its time containing, as it did, not only topographical maps but also some devoted to geological, meteorological, archaeological and natural history subjects. In conjunction with this work, John George produced a list of over 170 of the principal maps in the development of cartography. Atlas after atlas poured forth from the Edinburgh Geographical Institute under the guidance of this great cartographer. The most important production of all, **The Times Atlas**, was published in 1922 two years after his death.

In supporting the study of historical cartography, the Royal Scottish Geographical Society was also to play a vital role. John E. Shearer produced the first account of the mapping of Scotland in the Society's magazine (1905). Harry R.J. Inglis published a paper in three parts on the early maps of Scotland and their authors (1918, 1919). The ideas in his paper were to blossom into a full volume **The Early Maps of Scotland** which was published by the Society in 1934, with a second edition in 1936. This was to remain the standard work until it was replaced by D.G. Moir's two-volume third edition (1973, 1983). Their hard work has given fifty years of vital information to countless bands of scholars, while others have provided supplementary guides, for example the valuable guide to the literature of Scottish cartography by John N. Moore (1983).

The practice of cartography has also flourished in the universities. At Glasgow, Professor Gordon Petrie and John Keates have established a prestigious postgraduate school in topographic science and cartography, while computer mapping at Edinburgh has gained an international reputation. Remote sensing by satellite has given new insights into the resolution of many problems. An Aberdeen graduate, Colin Stove, developed the application of data from this source at the Macauley Institute and is now leading the Environmental Remote Sensing Applications Consultants (ERSAC) at Livingston.

Students of maps and cartography owe an inordinate debt to The National Library of Scotland for its efforts over the years to provide a service second to none (NLS 1984). The Map Room evolved as a separate unit only in 1958 with the creation of a new map reading room and storage space off the entrance hall in

George the IVth Bridge building. Its success was assured and for
the next few years, under the able superintendance of Miss Ann
Young,   there was a massive increase in usage and a vast inflow
of new material.   By 1974 it was necessary to move the Map
Section to an old biscuit factory in Causewayside.   The increased
space   allowed   the   relaxed   but   professional   service   to   be
continued even though the staff had to accommodate 40 tons of
material from the Ordnance Survey, vast holdings of 20th-century
War Office/ Ministery of Defence, Directorate of Colonial Survey/
Directorate of Overseas Survey maps, and copyright deposits from
Canada, New Zealand, Australia and the United States of America.
With a stock of over one and a quarter million sheet maps and
some fourteen thousand atlases, the National Library of Scotland
possesses   one   of   the   largest   and   most   comprehensive   map
collections   in   the   world.   Future   developments,   with   a   third
Map Room in the New Library Building that will house the Scottish
Science Reference Library,   will   ensure   a   bright   future   for
cartographic   studies   under   the   present   superintendent   Miss
Margaret Wilkes.

Indeed, Edinburgh is a cartographic treasure house for
scholars for, in addition to the National Library's Map Room,
there are substantial holdings in the Royal Scottish Geographical
Society, Scottish Record Office, the Library of the University of
Edinburgh and in the Department of Geography, Edinburgh City
Library, Scottish Air Photo Library, the Royal Society of
Edinburgh and the Institute of Geological Sciences.

The Royal Scottish Geographical Society, Bartholomews the
Mapmakers, the National Library of Scotland, the Scottish Record
Office and the Department of Geography at the University of
Edinburgh came together to host the IVth International Conference
on the History of Cartography in Edinburgh in 1971.   To mark the
occasion Bartholomews published **Maps of Scotland.**   This happy
cooperation between business and public and academic institutions
symbolizes our long tradition of working together to get Scotland
mapped.

4. REGIONAL SURVEYS

Alan Ogilvie, one of the founding figures of Scottish geography, declared the purpose of regional geography was "to describe the regions of a country as they are and to discover the causes that have made them what they are" (Ogilvie, 1953). Some geographers have explicitly sought an additional dimension for the goals of regional survey, namely as an input into policy-making and planning strategies. Although separated by several decades the writings of Patrick Geddes and Derek Diamond amply illustrate the genre.

When we remember the pre-eminent role of regional geography in teaching and research in the first half of the present century, the volume of writings related to the major regions of Scotland is remarkably limited. Amongst the most influential early studies were the three Scottish chapters in Ogilvie's **Great Britain** (1928, 1930, 1953), although the Scottish Geographical Magazine published some regional essays such as Huggins (1935) The Scottish Highlands - a regional study. The size of the academic market doubtless restricted the output for Geography was still a fledgling discipline in Universities and the school curriculum tended to emphasise regional geography of continents rather than countries. Certainly it would be misleading and erroneous to infer that the scale of publication on the regional geography of Scotland, or parts thereof, was a true yardstick of contemporary scholarship and research on this theme. Even in the post-war era of rapid expansion in geographical education there has scarcely been a flood of regional surveys. If we omit contributions in volumes on Great Britain or the British Isles there have only been a handful of texts on the geography of Scotland, (Rae and Brown, 1966 ; McIntosh and Marshall, 1966 ; Millman, 1974 ; Lea, Gordon and Bowler, 1977 ; Clapperton, 1983). There has, however, been an additional strand in regional survey which has assumed greater prominence in recent decades, namely the detailed analysis of particular regions. Thus the Highlands and Islands were the subject of surveys by O'Dell and Walton (1962) and, more recently, Turnock (1983). The Handbooks for British Association Conferences at Edinburgh (1951, 1979), Dundee (1968), Aberdeen (1963), Glasgow (1958) and Stirling (1974) contained major geographical surveys of the respective local regions as did the various county volumes of the **Third Statistical Account of Scotland.** Additionally, articles and monographs were published on the geography of particular districts, with islands recurrently attracting interest as illustrated by the study of **The Isle of Lewis and Harris** by Arthur Geddes (1955) and the various studies of Orkney by Ronald Miller (1959, 1976). Until the emergence of systematic geography in the late 1950s countless Honours dissertations contributed to the study of the regional geography of parts of Scotland and remain an important, if neglected, historical archive. More recently, the introduction of the Alternative syllabuses in Geography at Ordinary and Higher grade in Scotland prompted the production of resources including texts designed to illustrate the Scottish subject matter, e.g. Condie and McDonald (1983).

Some measure of the limited published material on the regional geography of Scotland in 1951 is provided by the fact that Alan Ogilvie, in his introductory chapter of **Scientific Survey of South-Eastern Scotland,** only refers to eight studies in the bibliography : two by himself, two by David Linton and one each by Mackinder, D. R. Macgregor, Andrew Learmonth and the early twentieth century geologists, Peach and Horne.

At the risk of gross oversimplification the regional surveys broadly adopted two methods of attack involving sub-regional treatment and/or topical accounts. Two Scottish chapters from Ogilvie's **Great Britain** illustrate these strategies. Thus John McFarlane in a study of North-East Scotland discussed the material under the headings ; Deeside, Donside, Aberdeen, Buchan, The Deveron and the Spey, the Spey to the Beauly Firth, Inverness Firth to Dornoch Firth, Sutherland and Caithness, Orkney and Shetland. By contrast, Ogilvie writing about Central Scotland initially used as the sub-headings certain aspects of the region, structure and minerals, land-forms, rivers and water supply, soils and vegetation, population and historical changes, and agriculture, before turning to sub-regions in the second half of the chapter. More recently the topical approach has become predominant, with different specialists contributing on particular themes. Thus Clapperton's volume **Scotland : a new study** (1983) is written by thirteen contributors with chapters on geological evolution, landforms, bio-climate, prehistoric regional dimensions, medieval rural settlements, rural settlement 1700-1850, urban settlement 1760-1980, transport systems, modern rural land use, fisheries, energy resources, manufacturing and future development.

Whatever approach is favoured the regional surveys all incorporated facets of the physical and man-made landscape and invariably included some consideration of temporal evolution and change of these landscapes and of man-made relationships. Many early analyses attached considerable explanatory importance to the factors of the physical environment although later studies have extended the causal web to include economic and social forces and choices, the balance of emphasis shifting with time, according to academic fashion and personal disposition.

Patrick Geddes contributed substantially to the development of regionalism. He was a doughty advocate of the region as a unit of investigation including in the Scottish setting his

Figure 6: Patrick Geddes

Dunfermline survey. Geddes followed the philosophy of Le Play in seeking to further our understanding of the interrelationships between environmental, cultural and economic factors. Geddes also argued for decentralisation, reconstruction of cultural and social life and radical social reform to remove the social, economic, psychological and cultural divisions between city and country. These social ideas had little impact outside of his close group of friends but Geddes left his mark in three differing ways. Firstly, at the local scale and practical level, efforts to counter cumulative 'dehousing' of the Old Town of Edinburgh included the building of students residences, whilst the Outlook Tower was a practical representation of many of his philosophical concepts. Secondly, the Geddesian view of regionalism had a profound influence on British regional geography throughout most of the first half of the present century. Thirdly, Geddes contributed to the advance of planning as a discipline by tirelessly promoting planning exhibitions, and undertaking surveys and preparing proposals. In this field he tapped the rich vein of a desire for order, development and improvement which is probably never far from the surface in any developed society. By the close of the Victorian era, local authorities had acquired wide-ranging powers of environmental control including the right to demolish unfit housing and build afresh. In the 1919 Housing Act, the provision of subsidies extended the statutory instruments by furnishing the means for the establishment of local authority housing estates. During the First World War planned settlements were built such as the small munitions village at Gretna and the more ambitious scheme for the development of a garden city at Rosyth. Additionally in 1913 Patrick Geddes and his future son-in-law, Frank Mears, planned a garden suburb near Leven but the project failed to materialise. Mears, however, became a leading figure in Scottish planning and played a major part in many surveys and plans including a study of Stirling in the 1930s and the influential **Regional Plan for Central and South-east Scotland (1948).** The latter was part of a trilogy of regional analyses of Central Scotland, the other components being surveys and plans for the Clyde Valley and Tayside, which formed the planks for post Second World War planning in the heartland of Scotland.

In the 1950s and 1960s this strand in regional surveys was sustained by both independent and commissioned research. Staff in the Geography Departments at Aberdeen and Glasgow surveyed different parts of the Highlands and Islands, e.g. Caird, Coull, Moisley, O'Dell. At the Scottish Development Department, Robert Grieve and Miss Baker introduced a strong geographical flavour into government surveys and plans. The Department of Social and Economic Research at Glasgow University, supported by other academics such as Derek Diamond, completed two government-commissioned surveys and plans for Lothians (1966) and Grangemouth-Falkirk (1968). In a similar fashion Dundee

University contributed to **Tayside : potential for development** (1970) and the Scottish Office completed this regional coverage by producing **The Central Borders : a plan for expansion** (1968). By the late 1960s the Scottish Development Department employed several geographers in regional and thematic surveys.

Staff in Geography Departments in the Scottish Universities were also engaged in regional analysis e.g. Stanley Jones, Keith Turner and David Pocock in Dundee. The academic and educational interests found outlets in the handbooks for conferences and regional atlases such as the Edinburgh Atlas (1966) edited by Wreford Watson and the Atlas of Glasgow and West Region of Scotland (1972) edited by Melvyn Howe.

Geography Departments are still engaged in regional research commissioned by national and local government but the immense growth in the establishments of the latter bodies has inevitably led to an increase in the data collection and proportion of research conducted by internal units and departments of the Regional and Island Councils and the Scottish Office. Equally, the varied skills required in planning surveys encouraged the engagement of firms of consultants, sometimes headed by geographers as in the case of Colin Buchanan for the transport survey and plan for Edinburgh (1972).

It is difficult to summarise regional surveys of Scotland, or parts of Scotland, but the species does display two recurrent characteristics, namely a sense of place and areal synthesis of geographical factors and phenomena. Enthusiasm about place and space is a fundamental mark of geographers and the writings of many practitioners in Scotland, such as Ogilvie, O'Dell and Watson, amply illustrate these qualities. The thrust of spatial synthesis has varied with academic fashion and the development of the subject. Invariably regional surveys have focused upon man-land relationships, normally including sections on the physical environment and on land and resource utilisation. Nonetheless the interest in community, society and way of life which underpinned the Geddesian approach and was subsequently developed by Fleure and others, has found expression in Scottish studies, especially of parts of the Highlands, e.g. Caird. The adoption of a positivist scientific stance in the late 1950s presented problems for regional surveys, for the emphasis shifted to generalisation, concepts, measurement and the specification of criteria and assumptions. More recent espousal of behavioural, humanistic and radical approaches to geographical analysis may lead to the introduction of exciting new vistas into regional geography, probably re-affirming a man-based view of spatial patterns. Whittington (1974) evaluated a different source of stimulus, the regional novel, in the specific form of the trilogy by Lewis Grassic Gibbon - **Sunset Song, Cloud Howe** and **Grey Granite.** He focussed attention on three components of Gibbon's novels ; the real and perceived landscape, group culture and regional consciousness. The regional novel not only offers a particular perception of landscapes, attitudes, places, communities, ways of life and relationships, but also introduces into regional analysis a further dimension which the geographer must evaluate along with other more traditional sources of information (Withers, 1984).

Equally whereas geology and the physical environment frequently constitute the touchstone of many regional surveys, modern studies would tend to adopt a more complex stance, examining linkages and patterns between the humanities, social sciences and environmental sciences through aspects such as history, culture, political institutions and legislative framework, settlement and built-form, economy, social policy, decision-making, climate, resources, soil and landforms.

The definitive regional survey will never be written because the multiplicity of facts, factors and variables defies such reduction but that should not deter geographers from striving for new goals and examining alternatives syntheses and approaches. It also should not detract from the extant heritage of scholarly geographical studies which have added greatly to our knowledge and understanding of the regional geography of Scotland.

5. HISTORICAL ROOTS

The study of our historical roots, at least in geographical terms, was on a modest scale until the last thirty years. The term "historical geography" was applied to the Scottish context for the first time in 1912 in W.R.A. Kermack's **The Making of Scotland - an Essay in Historical Geography.** In the early years of the twentieth century, the study of historical geography was firmly within the fields of human and regional geography. T.M. Steven's **A Geographical Description of the County of Ayr** (1912) and C.A. Scott's **The County of Renfrew** (1915) exemplify this approach (1929). Writers at this time followed the longstanding tradition of historical topography and saw themselves as general geographers to whom a knowledge of history was axiomatic (Mitchell and Cash, 1917).

As is usual in Scotland, the Highlands and Islands have attracted a disproportionate amount of attention and geographers have not been an exception. Much of the research has focused on the forces of agrarian change and depopulation since the mid-eighteenth century. This theme was initiated by J. Stewart in his study of change in Appin on Tayside (1911) and Ian D. Duff's comparable account of change in Wester Ross (1929). The Highland "Problem" was summed up by J. Mathieson who wrote on the Tragedy of the Highlands (1938). The historical implications of emigration also attracted attention with W.C.A. Ross's paper on Highland Emigration (1934). John D. Wood returned to the subject in his paper on Scottish Migration Overseas (1964).

Geographers of the modern school have been equally interested in this romantic area. The historical geography of the Hebrides has been studied by several scholars mainly in the Department of Geography in the University of Glasgow. James Caird's paper on Harris (1951) and **Park, a geographical study of a Lewis crofting district** (1959) were important pioneering works. H.A. Moisley, carried on with a series of studies of the Hebrides in the 1960s (1960, 1961, 1962, 1966). The romantic island of Skye has not attracted the same level of interest but M.D. McSween (1959) wrote a paper on the system of transhumance on the island. The West Highlands have been the focus of research by David Turnock (1967, 1969, 1975, 1977, 1979), Margaret Storrie (1961, 1962, 1965) and R.Alan Gailey (1960, 1961, 1962), each producing papers of great academic rigour on the historical changes from Sutherland to Argyll. Other writers have selected specific aspects of the Highland scene for detailed study: the kelp industry by L. Rhymer (1974) the shieling system by M.D. McSween (1959),R. A. Gailey (1961) and R. Miller (1967), rural housing by Gailey (1962) and Ian Whyte (1976), the introduction of sheep (Watson 1932, Innes 1983), and forestry and its associated industries by James Lindsay (1974, 1975, 1976, 1977).

It is not surprising therefore that **The Highlands and Islands of Scotland** by A.C. O'Dell and Kenneth Walton (1962), was one of the first university level geography texts on Scotland with eight chapters being devoted to the historical aspect.

The Northern Isles have also generated devoted research over the years especially by geographers from the University of Aberdeen. A.C. O'Dell began a long relationship with Shetland with his study of **Lerwick - a Port Study** (1934). His **The Historical Geography of the Shetland Islands** was a remarkable piece of work for its time but its publication in 1939 was soon overshadowed by world events. In post-war years James Coull continued Aberdeen University's links with the Northern Isles with a series of important papers about Orkney and Shetland (1964, 1966, 1967) and on the history of the fishing industry in that part of Scotland (1969, 1977). Ronald Miller's **Orkney** is an exceedingly useful regional description which uses the warp of history thoughout (1976).

It is a pity that the Lowlands and Borders have not been given the same attention as the Highlands and Islands. The influence of Patrick Geddes and his **Place, Folk, Work** is never far from the early studies in historical geography of Lowland Scotland. His son, Arthur, continued the father's wide interests but, even though he wrote voluminously, he never gained an academic reputation of distinction. His paper **The Changing Landscape of the Lothians 1600–1800 as revealed by Old Estate Plans"** (1938) illustrates how the study of the Lowlands has often focused on agrarian change especially in the eighteenth century. Land utilisation in Lanarkshire at the end of the eighteenth century was the subject of a pioneering paper by G. East (1937). J.H.G. Lebon wrote three papers on the change in landscape in Ayrshire (1946, 1952). For thirty years W.H.K. Turner has produced a series of well researched papers on the theme of the textile industry, especially that of Perthshire and Angus (1953, 1957, 1958, 1964, 1966, 1968, 1972). George Kay wrote on the landscape of improvement in the North East (1962). One of the most important papers on this subject was J. Caird's **The making of the Scottish rural landscape** (1964), while I.D. Whyte looked at the Lowland landscape in medieval and early modern times (1981). Planned villages have attracted the attention of geographers: J. M. Houston wrote a pioneering paper on the subject in 1946 and it has been followed by Douglas Lockhart who has devoted his career to these fascinating settlements (1978, 1979, 1980, 1982).

Had it not been for R.A. Dodgshon, the Borders would have received scant attention. He has published a series of very scholarly papers dealing with various aspects of land-holding and change in Berwickshire and Roxburghshire (1973, 1975) and on sheep farming during the age of improvement (1976). Few other

Figure 7: Alan Ogilvie

historical geographers have been attracted to this region although J.M. Houston wrote on the startling differences of landscape each side of the Border in the Solway Firth area (1949). The division of the commonty of Hassendean, near Hawick, has been the subject of detailed study by I.H. Adams (1971) and Martin Parry examined settlement and climatic change in the Lammermuirs (1973, 1975).

Detailed local studies, as are common in England, have not appeared in Scotland primarily because of the lack of a strong tradition of local history societies. The one major exception is the East Lothian Antiquarian and Field Naturalists' Society whose journal has carried several articles by historical geographers. I.H. Adams has written on the division of Dunbar Common (1977) and the runrigs of Tranent (1979) and I.D. White has examined grain growing (1977) and the grain trade (1979) in seventeenth-century East Lothian. The transactions of the Buchan Field Club have carried a paper by D.G. Lockhart on planned villages in the area (1979).

The affiliation between Geography and Archaeology has been very close in Scotland. Glasgow, Aberdeen, Dundee, St Andrews and Edinburgh have each produced geographer-archaeologists who have made important contributions in their joint discipline. For twenty years Horace Fairhurst produced a series of papers on the archaeology of rural settlement that were models of their kind. In Aberdeen Andrew O'Dell combined an interest in railways with Norse archaeology and in the latter field of interest produced one of Scotland's greatest archaological finds, "the St Ninian's Isle treasure." The subsequent controversy over whether it was Scotland's or Shetland's treasure somewhat overshadowed the intellectual worth of his achievement. His work in this field was carried on by Alan Small who took this interest with him to Dundee. The research into the medieval urban archaeology of St Andrews by Graeme Whittington and the appointment of Professor Bruce Proudfoot enabled the Department of Geography there to play a significant role in the establishment of archaeology in the university. A joint degree in geography and archaeology at the University of Edinburgh is clear evidence of the close relationships these departments have had for many years. Ian Morrison carries on this work with wide-ranging interests from Crannogs to underwater archaeology off the coasts of Scotland (1973, 1974).

The Modern School of Scottish Historical Geography

The stimulus for the development of a modern school of Scottish historical geography came about with the changing role of the Scottish Record Office. From time immemorial this

institution had been the preserve of the genealogist; even
Scottish historians were rarely found sheltering in its Adamesque
alcoves. Valuable estate records had been condemned to oblivion
as of no historic interest. Into this somnolent atmosphere came
four ex-servicemen - Andrew Anderson, John Bates, Peter
Goldsbourgh and John Imrie - who were to revolutionize the
institution. Of the four, Dr John Imrie, first as curator and
then as Keeper of the Records of Scotland, must be accorded the
distinction of instituting and then fulfilling a complete
reorganization of the archive. This was no mean task for the
volume of records - some fifty miles of shelves - and the lack of
indexing - some had been deposited on those very shelves over a
century earlier and had never been looked at - meant that the job
had to be started from scratch. What was recognized in this
renaissance was that the nature of historical inquiry was
changing and that they could take a lead in this change by
creating classes of records that would be relevant to the scholar
who was asking questions not about Mary Queen of Scots or Bonnie
Prince Charlie, but how everyday society went about its life and
business. From these dedicated public servants, scholars were
given not only access to previously unseen source material but
also were given a real sample of what public service can mean.

At Edinburgh a flourishing school of research started
inauspiciously with the appointment of Ian Adams to an editorship
at the Scottish Record Office. In this position, with the task of
editing the official List of Plans, he came to realise that the
importance lay not only in the maps and plans but also in the
muniments from which they had sprung. For his research on the
division of commonty in Scotland he used the processes of the
Court of Session, especially the extracted series, many of which
lay under the dust of two centuries. These studies led to the
publication of the **Descriptive List of Plans in the Scottish
Record Office**, (1966, 1970, 1974); and he became the first
geographer to contribute to the Scottish Record Society with his
Directory of former Scottish Commonties (1974). Martin Parry
brought an interdisciplinary approach by combining physical
geography and historical in his study of **Climate, agriculture and
settlement** (1978). The use of muniments and the Forfeited
Estates papers was pioneered by James Lindsay writing on forest
land use in Argyllshire and Perthshire (1975, 1976, 1977). The
problem of who owned the land in Scotland at the time of the
Improvements was tackled by Loretta Timperley and her painstaking
compilation of the lost valuation rolls led to the publication of
A Directory of Landownership in Scotland c.1770 (1976).

One of the most influential of the Edinburgh School is Ian
D. Whyte whose study of Scottish agriculture, a model of its
kind, appeared as **Agriculture and Society in Seventeenth-century
Scotland** (1979). Theses completed by the group include Kathleen

Hutchings' analysis of the structural change in Scottish
agriculture in the 19th century, while John Shaw took on the
monumental task of inventoring the watermills of Scotland (1983),
and R. Houston applied the most rigourous statistical analysis to
the emotive subject of the Clearances in surveying the impact of
economic change on the historical geography of Sutherland, 1791-
1891. Shetland was the focus of two studies : Jonathan Wills
undertook a detailed analysis of landlord-tenant relationships on
a nineteenth-century estate and the enigmatic character of
Shetland's scattalds was investigated by Susan Knox in her study
of agrarian change in Shetland in the 19th century. With a wide
variety of sources, including newly discovered series of volumes
by Robert Bald on the Scottish coal industry, George Wilson
(1980) wrote a thorough analysis of the Fife coal industry, 1750-
1914. Using the Seafield muniments, D.M. Munro combined a
detailed knowledge of ecology with historical and field evidence
to write on the environmental factors influencing rural land use
and society in Inverness and Moray since the mid-18th century.
Under the able editorship of Martin Parry and Terry Slater,
the Edinburgh School contributed to **The Making of the Scottish
Countryside** (1980).

Soon every geography department in Scotland provided
undergraduate teaching and research facilities in Scottish
historical geography. Douglas Lockhart joined J.B. Caird, A.
Small and W.H.K. Turner at the University of Dundee and continued
his work on the evolution of planned villages in North-east
Scotland. Outside Scotland, research has been undertaken by R.A.
Dodgshon at the Universities of Liverpool and Wales on agrarian
change in Roxburghshire and Berwickshire (1973, 1975).

There are still areas in which much work is required before
anything like a comprehensive understanding is attained. The
historical aspects of urban geography have lagged woefully behind
the study of rural Scotland. Some examples of the historical
geography of Scotland's cities have appeared in the pages of the
S.G.M. over the years: Aberdeen was described by J.R. Coull
(1963); Edinburgh by H.R.J. Inglis and W. Cowan (1919), Dundee by
S.G.E. Lythe (1938) and W.H.K Turner (1968); Glasgow by J.W.
Gregory (1921). Smaller burghs have not been totally neglected:
Arthur Geddes described Granton-on-Spey (1945) and Stornoway
(1947), and I.A.G. Kinniburgh the growth of Greenock and its
harbours (1960). A. C. O'Dell gave an account of Lerwick (1934)
while D.C.D. Pocock described Perth (1969).

The gap in our knowledge of urban Scotland is being filled,
however. I.H. Adams provided a sweeping historical survey in **The
Making of Urban Scotland** (1978). More detailed analysis on
various aspects of urbn geography are to be found in **Scottish
Urban History** (1983) edited by George Gordon and Brian Dicks. It
has chapters on the social and geographical structure of

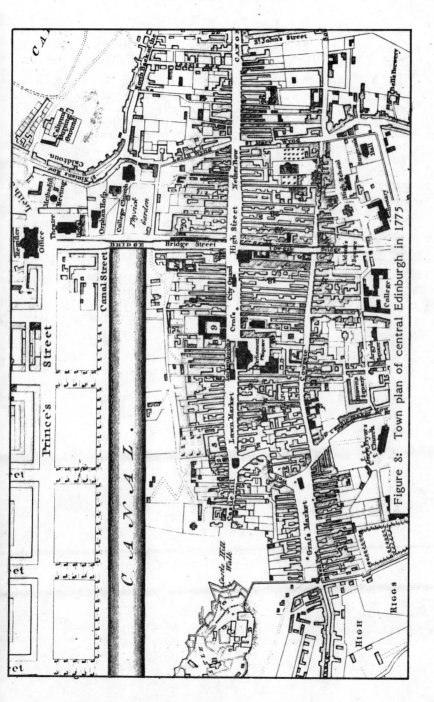

Figure 8: Town plan of central Edinburgh in 1775

Aberdeen, Edinburgh, Glasgow and Stirling.   Glasgow gained its first book by a geographer in Andrew Gibb's **Glasgow - the Making of a City,** (1983)

The early 1980s saw the coming of age of Scottish historical geography with the publication of several important books. David Turnock published his **Historical Geography of** Scotland since **1707** (1982) in which he took the theme of modernization, not just from 1707 but rather as a continuum from Anglo-Norman times. This theme has become the watchword for Scottish historical geographers and their colleagues in parallel disciplines.   In essence it is about economic, political, technological and social change and their impact on the evolving human geography of - not of North Britain - but of a separate entity, Scotland.   Chalmers M. Clapperton edited a work with an overwhelming emphasis on historical change, **Scotland: A New Study** (1983). Another book of oustanding importance is G. Whittington and I.D. Whyte's **An Historical Geography of Scotland** (1983) in which they bring together the leading writers in the field of historical geography to summarise the position to date.

6. PEOPLE, ECONOMY AND SOCIETY

In the hundred years since the founding of the R.S.G.S.
there have been substantial changes in the essential components
of human geography - the demographic and economic structure,
resources, way of life and social conditions of the whole country
and particular places or sections. From the heyday of
industrialisation we now face the arduous transformation to de-
industrialisation, with service jobs dominating the employment
structure and the threat of long-term high levels of unemployment
as technological development continues to reduce the need for
labour in traditional areas. The present trend differs
significantly from the earlier transformation from primary to
secondary activities because of the absence of a sufficient
creation of new employment opportunities to offset the impact of
decline and closure in existing activities. In the Victorian era
coal was the crucial indigenous natural resource; now it is the
oil extracted from beneath the North Sea. Whereas Glasgow could
once lay claim to the title, Second City of the Empire, the
decentralisation and dispersal of population since 1945 has now
reduced it to less than three-quarters of its maximum population.
Contemporaneously, five New Towns have been developed and change
(positive or negative) has affected other settlements and
regions.

The importance of these topics in planning and public policy
has partly been responsible for an upsurge in the last three
decades in a wide variety of geographical analysis of particular
facets of demography, economy and society. In the later
Victorian period these topics tended to be studied by members of
other disciplines, e.g. history, social statistics, medicine. It
was a few decades before studies penned by geographers began to
make a major contribution. This situation arose from the size of
the founding band of academic geographers and the diversity of
their interests, which included the study of distant lands,
supra-national themes and the physical environment. Chisholm
wrote a short article on density of population (1911) but there
was then a gap until Crowe (1927) published an analysis of **The
population of the Southern Lowlands.** Regional texts such as that
of Ogilvie (1928) incorporated a substantial amount of
information about population, resources and economic activities,
although social conditions and way of life were somewhat
neglected topics. With the growth of systematic fields of
geographical study, the literature was enriched with analyses of
agriculture, industry, settlement, resources and population based
upon a variety of spatial scales. Developmental or comparative
material frequently featured prominently although the emphasis
progressively switched to the investigation of locational
factors, policies, problems and processes.

For convenience, the subsequent discussion is divided into two sections dealing with People and Society and The Economic Dimension but it must be recognised that these are not rigid compartments of research and knowledge.

People and Society

Recent examples of the contemporary themes and approaches in geographical research related to people and society are provided by the contents of three volumes arising from symposia sponsored by the R.S.G.S. : **Where town meets country** (Cruickshank, 1981); **Quality of life and human welfare** (Pacione and Gordon, 1984); **Population change in contemporary Scotland** (Jones, 1984). Relevance, approach and practicalities were features of the contributions, whether in relation to land use in peri-urban areas, the quality of life or aspects of population change. Geographers edited the volumes but contributions were made by planners, ecologists, academics, technical advisers and officers of local authorities and of national bodies such as the Scottish Development Agency, the Countryside Commission for Scotland and the Forestry Commission. The mix of talents illustrated the aim of the symposia, which is ,to stimulate geographical discussion among a wide body of informed opinion on contemporary Scottish themes of major public interest.

It was the nineteenth century before the introduction of a decennial Census (1801) and the legal requirement to register births, deaths and marriages (1855) provided a comprehensive and reliable statistical data base for demographic analysis. In the middle of the eighteenth century Alexander Webster had used parish ministers as the statistical source for his census of population, a tradition which was followed by the compilers of the Old and New Statistical Accounts of Scotland. In the mid-Victorian period, medical officers were appointed by the major local authorities and the surveys and reports of men such as Henry Littlejohn in Edinburgh furnished a carefully documented analysis of the socio-medical geography of the various districts of the city. Within the discipline of geography, there was little research into the medical geography of Scotland until Melvyn Howe was appointed in 1967 to the Chair of Geography in the University of Strathclyde. In general, rigorous analysis of historical demographic sources and the pursuit of the many strands of investigation related to people and society has largely emerged within the last 20 to 30 years. In particular, census enumerators' books and some of the enormous store of documents in the Scottish Record Office have been used as sources in various historical studies of patterns and processes in rural and urban communities.

H. R. Jones has studied several aspects of population geography at both national and local scales. The latter spatial base attracted many geographers including Walton, Turnock, Soulsby and Storrie although Osborne (1958) adopted the national canvas for an historical analysis of migration. Historians made significant contributions to demograpjic research, notably in the seminal volume by Flinn **et al** (1977). Other important surveys included the Third Statistical Account of Scotland, the British Association handbooks and various planning reports.

Settlement geography has emerged as a major specialism with a substantial and varied literature covering diverse topics such as planned villages (Houston 1948, Lockhart 1978), land-use change in the city centre (Whitehand 1978, Sim 1982), urban morphology (Whitehand 1972, Gordon,1981), intra-urban migration (Forbes, Lamont and Robertson 1979) and aspects of urban social geography (Gordon 1979, Robb 1983, Kearsley and Srivastava 1974, Knox and MacLaran 1978, Knox and Pacione 1980). Social themes occupy a prominent place in current research. The analysis of processes, policies and problems is highlighted by work on housing supply and housing environments, urban deprivation, medical geography and service provision and the distribution of religious and linguistic groups. Gibb's thorough developmental account of Glasgow (1983) and Adams' authoritative survey of urbanisation and the evolution of urban landscapes illustrate another facet of urban literature.

A distinctive, if comparatively small, body of research has been produced on aspects of political geography. The electoral success of nationalism in the 1970s, the devolution referendum and the reorganisation of local government acted as catalysts to research but work has diversified into other areas of public policy and decision-making.

The economic dimension

Economic activities, land-use, resources, energy, transport and communications are long-standing subjects of geographical and public interest. Researchers have recognised the complex but crucial inter-relationships between these economic phenomena and social dimensions, although the balance of emphasis has varied with many studies concentrating on economic aspects.

Many regional texts have recognised the importance of energy resources, particularly the coal reserves of the Central Lowlands. Detailed studies of the Fife coalfield and coal markets were conducted by McNeil (1973) and Wilson (1980), the Scottish coalfields (Crowe, 1929) and the development of the Ayrshire (Lebon, 1933) and Stirling coalfields (Cadell, 1933).

By comparison, only a few studies have been made of some sources of energy e.g. hydro-electric power (Lea, 1969), although Baily did speculate on the potential of water power in 1931.   Keith Chapman has been the principal geographical contributor on the development of North Sea oil and gas and the Department of Geography at Aberdeen University have also undertaken considerable research on the environmental impact of developments related to these energy resources.   Recent evaluation of alternative sources of power, such as peat, has been the product of work in other disciplines.

The Scottish fishing industry during the last one hundred years has experienced considerable changes with respect to economic importance, size and type of catch, location of fishing grounds, ports and transport and in the structural organisation of the industry.   One of the earliest geographical studies was that by Stewart on the Scottish Herring Industry (1931), but the major contribution has been by J. R. Coull.

Forestry, farming and certain aspects of recreation and tourism fall within the compass of the term, rural land use. These topics have attracted the attention of human and physical geographers with the biogeographical research of Joy Tivy, the first female professorial Scottish geographer, providing an outstanding example of the environmental approach.   The activities of the Forestry Commission have inevitably tended to dominate Scottish studies of forestry, but with more than 60,000 farms and holdings, pursuing a wide variety of farming practices, surveys of agriculture and livestock husbandry have displayed considerable variation in approach, scale and topical definition. Some indication of the range is provided by the contrast between the comprehensive cartographic analysis in Coppock's (1976) **An Agricultural Atlas of Scotland,** the established tradition of regional surveys of farming (e.g. Ogilvie, 1928) and the detailed studies of one crop, or the impact of a particular innovation or policy. The man-land nexus featured in an article by Snodgrass (1933), sometime editor of the S.G.M., entitled **Stock farming and its relation to environment.** In recent years tourism and recreation have become important facets of the Scottish economy, a feature illustrated in the array of commissioned research emanating from the Tourism and Recreation Research Unit, Department of Geography, Edinburgh University.

Strangely, there was a marked absence of articles on Scottish industry in the first fifty volumes of the S.G.M. Chisholm (1910) wrote a fascinating discussion of market accessibility which challenged Weber's thesis of industrial location, but his article only made fleeting reference to printing and publishing in Edinburgh as examples of market association.   Robertson (1958) also introduced concepts and techniques from other disciplines in a study of locational and

Figure 9: Four facets of the Scottish economy: farming, Livingston New Town, electricity generating scheme in Galloway and fishing

structural aspects of industry in Edinburgh.   Studies of specific
industries were produced for shipbuilding (Campbell 1964), whisky
(Storrie,1962, MacPherson, 1964), textiles (Turner 1953, 1957,
1964, 1966)and iron and steel (Warren, 1965).   Structural change
was investigated regionally (Carter, 1974, Welch 1974) and in
relation to immigrant firms (Welch, 1970), new firm formation
(Gross, 1980), oil related industry (Turnock, 1977), the role of
the New Towns in industrial growth (Robertson, 1964) and office
activity (Fernie, 1979).   At the macro scale Gordon (1983) wrote
an overview of industrial development, 1750-1980.   Additionally,
geographers cited the work of economists and economic historians,
of the Scottish Council, Scottish Development Agency and Scottish
Development Department.   A similar situation existed in relation
to the study of transport and communication, but in this instance
contributions from other disciplines were predominant.   Examples
of geographical studies included commissioned research for the
Highland and Islands Development Board by Farrington et al
(1978,1981) and articles of air services to the Northern Isles
(Coulland Willis 1970), Hebridean car ferries (Turnock 1965),
Clydeport (Kinniburgh 1966), historical studies of roads (Moir
1957) and the carrier trade (Morris 1980) and impact studies of
the Tay and Forth Road bridges (Jones and Pocock 1966, Macgregor
1966).

Apart from studies of the manufacturing sector of cities
such as that of Dundee (Pacione 1972), land use and service
functions of urban settlements also fall within the province of
the economic dimension.   The conflict for space in and around
settlements featured in Diamond's (1962) analysis of the central
business district of Glasgow and Barke's (1974) historical study
of the rural-urban fringe of Falkirk.   By comparison, central
place studies (e.g. Pocock 1968) stressed connectivity in space.

In 1943 Catherine Snodgrass published in the S.G.M. a map of
economic regions of Scotland (Fig. 10) aimed at 'people engaged
in research preliminary to planning'.   She saw her map as an
interim working base awaiting detailed local and regional
research.   Ten regions were identified, namely :

1.   Highlands   (1A Central and Northwest Highlands,
                    1B Southern Uplands
                    1C Isolated hill masses of the Lowlands).

2.   The Far North cattle and sheep rearing region

3.   The Northeast cattle and sheep rearing region

4.   The East Coast mixed farming region with concentration on crop
      production in the lower coastal districts

5.   Tweed valley sheep rearing and mutton producing region

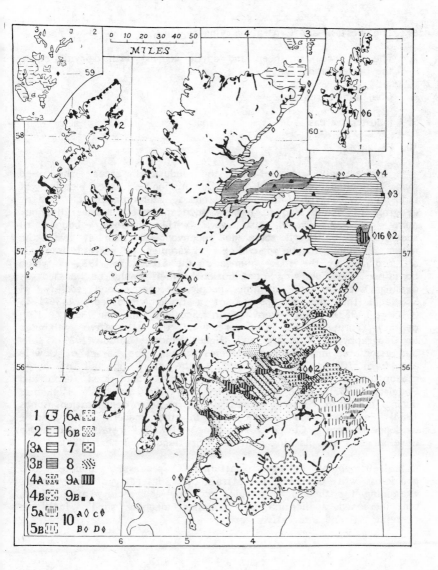

Figure 10: Economic regions of Scotland (Snodgrass, 1943)

6.   The Western and Central dairying region

7.   The Southwestern sheep and cattle rearing with dairying on the better land

8.   Coal mining regions

9.   Industrial areas

10. Fisheries

Interestingly, in defining the industrial areas, she used maps compiled for the Royal Commission on the location of industry by David Linton, the noted geomorphologist.   Many geographers would tend to eschew such macro-scale generalisation; many of them would also work within narrower bounds of specialisation, although some do endeavour to span at least the major divisions of the discipline.   Examples of currect interests are provided by the four volumes of the S.G.M. for 1983-84 which contained the following contributions which could be classed as dealing with aspects of the people, economy and society of Scotland: the monastic record of a Border landscape, 1136-1236 (Gilbert 1983); flax weaving in Scotland in the early 19th century (Turner 1983); the spread of the alternative syllabuses in Geography at Ordinary and Higher grades (Gordon 1983); soils and associated management problems within the Carses of Gowrie and Earn (Gauld and Bell, 1983); the rise and fall of burgh monopolies in Scotland - the case of the North East (Gibb and Paddison 1983); land use changes in the Scottiash Highlands during the 19th century - the role of pasture degeneration (Innes 1983); neighbourhood communities in the modern city - some evidence from Glasgow (Pacione 1983); retail warehouse developments and planning policies in Scotland (P. Jones, 1984).

Development, change, patterns, processes, policies and problems will continue to attract the interest of geographers examining the themes of people, economy and society of Scotland, but increased application of computer mapping should facilitate correlational and integrative work.

7. CONTINUITY AND CHANGE

A fundamental objective of the Society at its inception was the improvement of geographical teaching and knowledge in Scotland. Since higher education in geography was virtually non-existent, it instituted prizes, open by competition, to pupils in schools in country districts. Courses were organised, for teachers and the general public, and held in the Society's rooms in the National Portrait Gallery, Queen Street. An early ambition was to secure the establishment of a Chair, or at least a Lectureship in Geography at the University of Edinburgh and on 20th January, 1908, George Chisholm was appointed. Previously, a lectureship was started in the Heriot-Watt College in Physiography and Commercial Geography and filled by H. R. Mill in 1887. At the same time, Patrick Geddes was the initiator of a scheme of University extension lectures and Mill, again a staunch supporter, used the new method of optical projection or slides which the Society had encouraged from its beginning.

Chisholm was the ideal choice as the pioneer academic geographer. There were those unwilling to accept the discipline as worthy of university recognition, but Chisholm, with a mastery of facts and an exceptional gift of summarising them, achieved authority and respect by avoiding overstatement and justifying every opinion. When Readerships were established in Edinburgh in 1919, his was the first appointment. Lectureships quickly followed at Glasgow and at Aberdeen after the first World War. The first Chair was endowed at Edinburgh in 1931 and occupied by Alan Ogilvie. Links with the Society have been maintained through the award of the Scottish Universities medal to geography students for meritorious work at each of the Universities since the first award at Edinburgh in 1909.

The graduates from these departments have, in turn, made geography both a vital and a popular subject in schools. The Scottish Association of Geography Teachers (SAGT) is a thriving and active organisation which publishes regular bulletins, some in conjunction with the R.S.G.S. Through their enthusiasm, pupils learn both new skills and attitudes relevant to the modern world and an appreciation of the characteristics of the Scottish environment. The founding aim of the Society remains in good hands while wider interest in geographical matters is demonstrated by the popularity of television programmes such as 'Horizon' or 'The World About Us'.

If the Society introduced a new era in 1884 by bringing the leading explorers of the world to Scotland, today, with the proliferation of manned satellites and the first move off the planet to the moon, with instant coverage of sporting and international events by television so that the world can watch simultaneously, there is no longer any doubt that we live on one earth. The problems of any part of the globe, be it drought or war, is immediately known and the concern of all of us is involved. Technological innovation permits new horizons and appreciation of problems at scales ranging from the locality to the globe. With them come a change in attitude and an ever growing awareness that, in John Donne's words 'no man is an island'.

Few technological developments are more exciting geographically than the use of orbital or geosynchronous remote sensing satellites. These perform various functions but the monitoring of meteorological and other environmental conditions, the survey of natural rsources and the ability to map human settlements and infrastructure provide a vast and invaluable data source. It is always worth emphasising, however, that ground control remains essential and data acquired by remote sensors must be interpreted against accumulated knowledge of particular places. In Scotland, the meteorological satellites are tapped for data, transposed into pictures for ease of understanding, and made available by the University of Dundee. At the same time, the ability to manipulate such large volumes of data for analysis and presentation is crucial and the development of geographical information systems for this purpose represents a major area of study in geography well represented at the University of Edinburgh. No one can comprehend vast and complex tables of data and, as happened in the past, computer mapping techniques for visual presentation have been devised of which GIMMS, created at Edinburgh, is widely used in British universities. Equally, the contruction of geographical gazetteers is now a problem in database management and, increasingly, information of this nature will be accessible via visual displays on television.

Technology alone will not alter our comprehension of Scotland. The ability to utilise and apply this knowledge is crucial and, fortunately, the influence of geographers has spread. Within the Scottish Development Department geographers have found their basic training and the flexibility of mind, which is the hallmark of a geographical education, of considerable value in tackling the many and diverse problems in which government is involved today. Conservation groups and environmentalists require a sound geographical background if their arguments are to have any weight whatever, and general appreciation of the basic man-land relationship has become widespread. Many policies are geographically based and the need for data organised accordingly. Above all, census data on the population of Scotland is vital to any future projection. When the age-sex ratio of the country is calculated (Fig. 12) for the end of the century the implications in terms of service provision, employment requirements and economic cost start to become apparent.

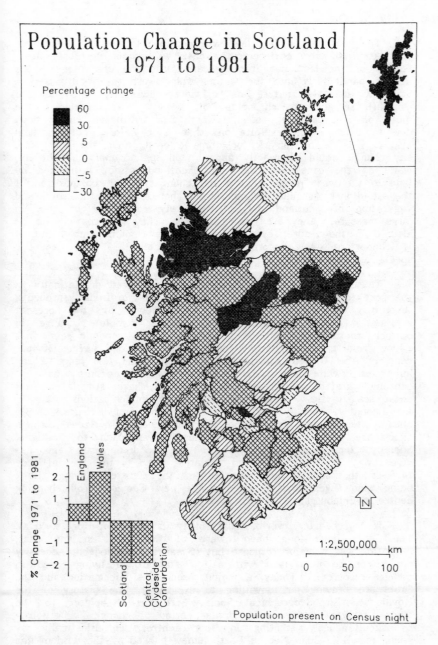

Figure 11: Population change in Scotland, 1971-1981

The geography of Scotland will continue to be made. Further elucidation of the environmental past will come not only from studies of the land but from research into the character of the oceans, particularly into the waters which wash the West coast of Scotland and the nature of offshore sediments, in order to establish an accurate chronology of change. In climatology, the meteorological conditions of the North Sea are better known now, due to offshore oil exploitation, than ever before, but Scotland also provides a benchmark for climatic change. On the one hand, any change would be readily apparent in such a marginal climate, while on the other the fact that Scotland is not influenced by land to the west means that global changes in the composition of the atmosphere should be measurable here. Both the soils and vegetation of Scotland are of relatively recent origin and, in large measure, they are now man made. They will continue to be altered in the future, even if the climate remains stable, but it is important to record their characteristics in generally specialised environments.

The human geography of Scotland has altered dramatically in the past forty years and will continue to do so. Living through a revolution is never easy and the effects of the present information based upheaval necessitates a complete change in outlook, social habits and circumstances. The economic scene has swung from traditional heavy industries to Scotland having 30 per cent of the United Kingdom's electronic and knowledge based industries, while the Clyde ports have declined as oil, container traffic and proximity to Europe have stimulated east coast sea traffic. Constantly improving communications open up the country, particularly for recreation and leisure, while cheap international air transport extends mental horizons through experience and stimulates a comparative approach to Scotland. Socially, the isolation hospital of one hundred years ago has given way to the need for geriatric care while the attitude towards the sabbath is reflected in the Trustee Savings Bank being open seven days a week in the new Cameron Toll shopping centre in Edinburgh.

In a changing world, adaptability is essential for survival. The Scots have long been aware of this fact. In the past, migration was a major response but it was a movement of necessity not of choice in a land with a low standard of living based on meagre resources. Today, a major resource is information and the Scots are proving not unwilling to exploit it. The history of the Royal Scottish Geographical Society provides a pointer to the future. It was founded in a similar period of change ambitiously by simultaneously starting in four centres, enthusiastically by young men like John George Bartholomew backed by the wisdom and practical guidance of men like James Geikie and John Murray, democratically by being open to all, including women, unlike its counterpart the Royal Geographical Society, and sustained by a

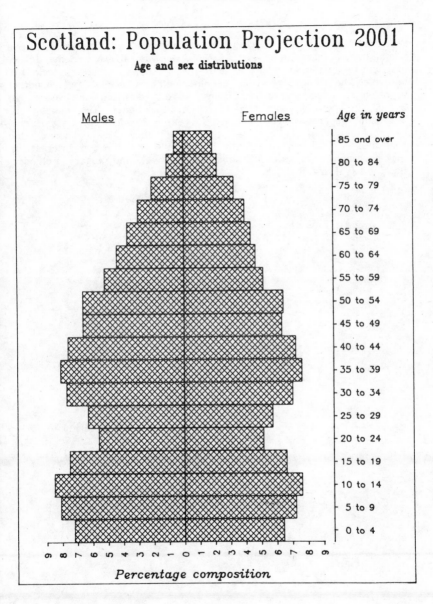

Figure 12: Age-sex ratio projection for 2000 AD

readiness to accept fresh opportunities and responsibilities. Some things take time - in 1884 there was a great demand for metrication, decimal coinage and the twenty-four hour clock all of which have only recently become commonplace. Two hundred years ago, geographical conditions largely dictated the mode of living, the outlook, and the habits of the Scots. The making of Scottish geography has given great freedom from direct geographical controls but, at the same time, has enhanced the character and charm of Scotland. This alone will keep interest in the geography of Scotland alive and active, and augers well for the future of the R.S.G.S.

REFERENCES

Adams, I. H.

1958 **John Horne's survey of Assynt.**
Edinburgh. Scottish History Society.

1966 **Descriptive list of plans in the Scottish Record Office.** 3 vols. (1966, 1970, 1973). H.M.S.O.

1967 Large scale manuscript plans in Scotland.
Journal of the Society of archivists 3 : 286-90.

1968 The land surveyor and his influence on the Scottish rural landscape. **S.G.M. 84** : 248-55.

1971 Division of the commonty of Hassendean, 1761-3.
The Stair Society Miscellany, : 181-92.

1973 **John Ainslie, land surveyor.**
Edinburgh. Scottish Record Office.

1975 George Taylor - surveyor o'pairts.
Imago Mundi 27 : 55-63.

Economic progress and the Scottish land surveyor.
Imago Mundi 27 : 13-18.

1976 Sources for Scottish local history-5 : Estate Plans.
The Local Historian 12 : 26-30.

1978 **The making of urban Scotland.** London. Croom Helm.

1979 **Papers on Peter May, Land Surveyor, 1749-1793.**
Edinburgh. Scottish History Society.

The division of the runrigs of Tranent.
Trans. East Lothian Antiquarian Soc. 26 : 25-36.

1984 One hundred years later : does Scotland exist ?
S.G.M. 100 : 123-134.

Adams, I. H. and Fortune, G. (eds)

1980 **Alexander Lindsay. A rutter of the Scottish Seas.**
Maritime Monograph No. 44. Greenwich. National Maritime Museum.

Agassiz, L.
    1840 On the evidence of the former existence of glaciers in
         Scotland, Ireland and England.
         Proc. Geol. Soc. London 3 : 327-32.

Baily, F. G.
    1931 Water power resources of Scotland. **S.G.M. 47** : 129-44.

Baird, P. D. and Lewis, W. V.
    1957 The Cairngorm floods, 1956, **S.G.M. 73** : 91-100.

Ballantyne, C. K.
    1979 A sequence of Lateglacial ice-dammed lakes in East
         Argyll. **Scott. J. Geol. 15** : 153-60.

Ballantyne, C. K. and Waine-Hobson, T.
    1980 The Loch Lomond Advance on the island of Rhum.
         Scott. J. Geol. 16 : 1-10.

Barclay, J. B. (ed)
    1979 **Looking at Lothian.** Edinburgh. R.S.G.S.

Barke, M.
    1974 The changing urban fringe of Falkirk ; some
         geographical implications of urban growth.
         S.G.M. 90 : 85-97.

Bartholomew, John and Sons, Ltd.
    1971 **Maps of Scotland.** Edinburgh. John Bartholomew.

Birks, H. H. et al
    1975 Pollen maps for the British Isles 5000 years ago.
         Proc. Roy. Soc. Lond. (B) 189 : 87-105.

Birse, E. L.
    1971 **Assessment of climatic conditions in Scotland, No.3.
         The bioclimatic sub regions.**
         Aberdeen. Macauley Institute.

Bremner, A.
    1942 The origin of the Scottish river system.
         S.G.M. 58 : 15-20, 54-58, 99-102.

Buchanan, Colin
    1972 **Edinburgh : the recommended plan.**

Burnett, J. H. (ed)
    1964 **The vegetation of Scotland.** Edinburgh.

Cadell, H. M.
    1904 The industrial development of the Forth valley.
         S.G.M. 20 : 66-84.

    1913 **The story of the Forth.** Glasgow. James Maclehose.

    1933 The Stirling coalfield. **S.G.M. 49 :** 229-30.

Caird, J. B.
    1951 The Isle of Harris. **S.G.M. 67 :** 85-100.

    1959 **Park : a geographical study of a Lewis crofting
         district.** Glasgow.

    1964 The making of the Scottish rural landscape.
         S.G.M. 80 : 72-80.

    1972 Changes in the Highlands and Islands of Scotland.
         Geoforum 12.

    1979 Land use in the Uists since 1800.
         Trans. Roy. Soc. Edin. 77B : 505-526.

         The making of the crofting landscape.
         J. Scott. Assoc. Geog. Teachers 8 : 7-25.

Campbell, R. H.
    1964 Scottish shipbuilding : its rise and progress.
         S.G.M. 80 : 107-113.

Carter, C.
    1974 Some changes. in the post war industrial geography of
         the Clydeside Conurbation. **S.G.M. 90 :** 14-26.

Caseldine, C. and Mitchell, W. A. (eds)
    1974 **Problems of the deglaciation of Scotland.**
         St. Andrews.

Cash, C. G.
    1901 The first topographical survey of Scotland.
         S.G.M. 27 : 399-413.

    1907 Manuscript maps by Pont, the Gordons and Adair in the
         Advocates Library, Edinburgh. **S.G.M. 23 :** 514-92.

Chapman, K.
    1976 **North Sea oil and gas : a geographical perspective.**
         Newton Abbot. David and Charles.

Chisholm, G.
   1910 The geographical relation of the market to the seats of
        industry. **S.G.M. 26** : 169-82.

Clapperton, C. M.
   1977 **North-east Scotland : geographical essays.** Aberdeen.

Clapperton, C. (ed)
   1983 **Scotland : a new study.**
        Newton Abbot. David and Charles.

Common, R.
   1954 A report on the Lochaber, Appin and Benderloch floods,
        May, 1953. **S.G.M. 70** : 6-20.

   1956 The Border floods, 1956. **S.G.M. 72** : 160-162.

Condie, I. and MacDonald, D.
   1983 **Scotland : geographical studies.**

Coppock, J. T.
   1976 **An agricultural atlas of Scotland.**
        Edinburgh. John Donald.

Coull, J. R.
   1963 The historical geography of Aberdeen.
        S.G.M. 79 : 80-94.

        Melness : a crofting community on the north coast of
        Sutherland. **Scot. Stud. 7** : 135-49.

   1964 Walls : a Shetland crofting parish.
        S.G.M. 80 : 135-49.

   1966 The economic development of the island of Westray,
        Orkney. **S.G.M. 82** : 154-68.

        Population trends and structures on the island of
        Westray, Orkney. **Scot. Stud. 10** : 69-77.

   1968 Modern trends in Scottish fisheries.
        S.G.M. 84 :15-28.

   1969 Fisheries in the north east of Scotland before 1800.
        Scot. Stud 13 : 17-32.

   1977 Fisheries in Scotland in the 16th., 17th. and 18th.
        centuries. The evidence in Macfarlane's geographical
        collection. **S.G.M. 93** : 5-14.

Coull, J. R. and Willis, P. D.
   1970 The air services in the North Isles of Orkney.
        Geography 55 : 204-8.

Craig, G. Y. (ed)
   1983 **Geology of Scotland.** (2nd Edtn.)
        Edinburgh. Scottish Academic Press.

Crosbie, A.J., Crosbie, N. J. and Dick, I.H.A.
   1968 **Air pollution in Edinburgh : Vol. 1 the background to
        research.** Edinburgh. Department of Geography,
        University of Edinburgh.

Cross, M.
   1981 **New firm formation and regional development.**
        London. Gower.

Crowe, P. R.
   1927 The population of the Southern Lowlands.
        S.G.M. 43 : 147-167.

   1929 The Scottish coalfields. **S.G.M. 45** : 321-37.

Cruickshank, A. (ed)
   1981 **Where town meets country.**
        Aberdeen University Press/R.S.G.S.

Cullingford, R. A. and Smith, D. E.
   1966 Lateglacial shorelines in eastern Fife.
        Trans. Inst. Br. Geogr. 39 : 31-51.

Davies, G. L.
   1968 The tour of the British Isles made by Louis Agassiz in
        1840. **Annals of Science 24** : 131-46.

Dewdney, J. C.
   1955 Changes in population in the County of Fife, 1755-1951.
        S.G.M. 71 :27-42.

Diamond, D. R.
   1960 The central business district of Glasgow.
        IN Norborg, K. (ed)
        Lund I.G.U. Symposium in urban geography.

Dodgshon, R. A.
   1973 The nature and development of infield-outfield in
        Scotland. **Trans. Inst. Br. Geogr. 59** : 1-23.

   1975 Towards an understanding and definition of runrig ; the
        evidence for Roxburghshire and Berwickshire.
        Trans. Inst. Br. Geogr. 64 : 15-33.

Runrig and the communal origins of property in land.
The Juridicial Review, 1975 - 189-208.

Farming in Roxburghshire and Berwickshire on the eve of
improvement. **Scot. Hist. Rev.** *54* : 140-154.

Scandinavian 'Solskifte' and the sunwise division of
land in eastern Scotland. **Scot. Stud.** 19 : 1-14.

1976 The economics of sheep farming in the Southern Uplands
during the age of improvement.
Econ Hist. Rev., 2nd. Series, 29 : 551-69.

Duff, I. D.
1929 The human geography of southwest Ross-shire, 1800-1920.
S.G.M. *45* : 277-95.

Durno, S. E.
1956 Pollen analysis of peat deposits in Scotland.
S.G.M. 73 : 177-87.

1957 Certain aspects of vegetational history in north-east
Scotland. **S.G.M. 73** : 176-84.

1958 Pollen analysis of peat deposits in eastern Sutherland
and Caithness. **S.G.M. 74** : 127-35.

1959 Pollen analysis of peat deposits in the eastern
Grampians. **S.G.M. 75** : 102-111.

East, G.
1937 Land utilisation in Lanarkshire at the end of the
eighteenth century. **S.G.M. 33** : 89-110.

Elgood, L. A. (ed)
1961 **Natural resources in Scotland.**
Edinburgh. Scottish Council (Development and Industry).

Fairhurst, H.
1939 The natural vegetation of Scotland : its character and
development. **S.G.M. 55** : 193-211.

1964 The surveys for the Sutherland clearances 1813-20,
Scot. Stud. 8 : 1-18.

1968 An old estate plan of Auchindrain, mid-Argyll.
Scot. Stud. 12 : 183-7.

Farrington, J. H. and Stanley, P. A.
1978 **Public transport in Skye and Lochalsh.** H.I.D.B.

Farrington, J. H., Stanley, P. A. and Bain, S. M.
1979 **Public transport in northwest Sutherland.** H.I.D.B.

Fernie, J.
1979 Office activity in Edinburgh. **Ekistics 275** : 25-32.

Findlay, A. M.
1978 "Cuninghamia" : Timothy Pont's contribution to Scottish cartography re-examined, **S.G.M. 94** : 36-47.

Flinn, M., Gillespie, J. et al
1977 **Scottish population history from the seventeenth century to the 1930s.** Cambridge University Press.

Forbes, J., Lamont, D. and Robertson, I.
1979 **Intra-urban migration in Greater Glasgow.** Central Research Unit, Scottish Development Department.

Fox, R. C.
1979 The morphological, social and functional districts of Stirling. **Trans. Inst. Br. Geogr. New Series 4** : 153-167.

Freeman, T. W.
1976 The Scottish Geographical Magazine - its first thirty years. **S.G.M. 92** : 92-100.

Gailey, R. A.
1960 Settlement and population in Kintyre 1750-1800. **S.G.M. 76** : 99-107.

1961 Mobility of tenants on a Highland estate in the early nineteenth century. **Scot. Hist. Rev. 40** : 136-54.

The role of sub-leyying in the crofting community. **Scot. Stud. 5** : 57-76.

1962 The evolution of Highland rural settlement. **Scot. Stud. 6** : 155-77.

The peasant houses of the South West Highlands of Scotland. **Giverin 3** : 227-42.

1963 Agrarian improvement and the development of enclosure in the southwest Highlands of Scotland. **Scot. Hist. Rev. 42** : 105-25.

Gardiner, Leslie
1976 **Bartholomew 150 years.** Edinburgh. John Bartholomew & Sons.

Gardiner, R. A.
    1977 William Roy, surveyor and antiquary.
        Geog. J. 143 : 439-450.

Garnett, A.
    1939 Diffused light and sunlight in relation to relief
        settlement in high latitudes. **S.G.M.** 55 : 271-284.

Gauld, J. H. and Bell, J. S.
    1983 Soils and associated management problems within the
        Carses of Gowrie and Earn. **S.G.M.** 99 : 77-88.

Geddes, Arthur
    1938 The changing landscape of the Lothians 1600-1800 as
        revealed by old estate plans. **S.G.M.** 54 : 128-43.

    1955 **The Isle of Lewis and Harris.**

Geikie, Archibald
    1901 **The scenery of Scotland.** (3rd Edtn.) London. Macmillan.

Geikie, James
    1894 **The Great Ice Age.** (3rd Edtn.) London.

    1905 **Structural and field geology.**
        Edinburgh. Oliver and Boyd.

Gemmell, A. M. D. (ed)
    1975 **Quaternary studies in north-east Scotland.** Aberdeen.

Gibb, A.
    1983 **Glasgow - the making of a city.** London. Croom Helm.

Gibb, A. and Paddison, R.
    1983 The rise and fall of burghal monopolies : the case of
        the North East. **S.G.M.** 99 : 130-140.

Gilbert, J.
    1983 The monastic record of a Border landscape.
        S.G.M. 99 : 4-15.

Gloyne, R. W.
    1966 Some features of the climate of the immediate area
        served by the Forth and Tay road bridges.
        S.G.M. 82 : 110-118.

Goodier, R. (ed)
    1974 **The natural environment of Scotland.** Edinburgh.

Gordon, G.
    1979 The status areas of early to mid-Victorian Edinburgh.
         Trans. Inst. Br. Geogr. NS4 : 168-91.

    1981 Thehistorico-geographicexplanationofurban
         morphology : discussion of some Scottish evidence.
         S.G.M. 97 : 16-26.

    1983 The spread of the Alternative Syllabuses in Geography
         at Ordinary and Higher grades. **S.G.M. 99** : 31-43.

Gordon, G. and Dicks, B. (eds)
    1983 **Scottish urban history** Aberdeen University Press.

Gray, J. M. and Lowe, J. J. (eds)
    1977 **Studies in the Scottish Lateglacial environment.**
         Oxford.

Gregory, J. W.
    1921 Glasgow and its geographical history. **S.G.M. 37** : 2-12.

Halstead, C. A.
    1956 Climatic observations in Scotland. **S.G.M. 72** : 21-3.

Hamilton, P.
    1963 The climate of Aberdeen. **S.G.M. 79 :** 74

Houston, J. M.
    1948 Village planning in Scotland, 1745-1845.
         Advancement of Science 5 : 129-133.

    1949 The rural settlements of the Solway Firth plain.
         I.G.U. CRCIG Lisbon, tome III : 421-6.

Howe, G.Melvyn (ed)
    1972 **Atlas of Glasgow and the West Region of Scotland.**
         Holmes McDougall.

Howe, G. Melvyn
    1982 London and Glasgow : a spatial analysis of mortality
         experience in contrasting metropolitan centres.
         S.G.M. 98 :

Huggins, K. M.
    1935 The Scottish Highlands : a regional study.
         S.G.M. 51 : 296-306.

Inglis, H. R. G.
    1918 Early maps of Scotland and their authors (maps in the
         library of the Royal Scottish Geographical Society).
         S.G.M. 34 : 217-230, 378-386.

John Adair : an early map-maker and his work.
S.G.M. 34 : 60-65.

1919 Early maps of Scotland and their authors.
S.G.M. 35 : 41-6.

1923 The Wade maps and other additions to the Society's collection. **S.G.M. 39** : 181-3.

1936 **The early maps of Scotland.**

Inglis, H. R. G. and Cowan, W.
1919 The early maps and views of Edinburgh.
S.G.M. 35 : 315-27.

Innes, J. L.
1983 Land use changes in the Scottish Highlands during the nineteenth century : the role of pasture degeneration.
S.G.M. 99 : 141-149.

Jardine, W. G.
1959 River developments in Galloway. **S.G.M. 75** : 65-74.

Jones, H. R.
1970 Migration to and from Scotland since 1960.
Trans. Inst. Br. Geogr. 49 : 145-159.

1975 A spatial analysis of human fertility in Scotland.
S.G.M. 91 : 102-113.

Jones, H. R. (ed)
1984 **Population change in contemporary Scotland.**
Geobooks/R.S.G.S. Norwich.

Jones, H. R. and Pocock, D. C. D.
1966 Some economic and social implications of the Tay Road Bridge. **S.G.M. 82** : 93-103.

Jones, S. (ed)
1968 **Dundee and district.** British Association, Dundee.

Kearsley, G. W. and Srivastava, S. R.
1974 The spatial evolution of Glasgow's Asian community.
S.G.M. 90 : 110-124.

Kemp, D. D.
1976 Buried raised beaches on the northern side of the Forth valley, central Scotland. **S.G.M. 92** : 120-128.

Kermack, W. R. A.
    1912 The making of Scotland - an essay in historical
         geography. **S.G.M. 28** : 295-305.

Kinniburgh, I. A. G.
    1960 John Ainslie's map of Port Glasgow in 1806.
         S.G.M. 76 : 23-4.

    1966 New developments in Clydeport. **S.G.M. 82** : 144-153.

    1968 A note on Timothy Pont's survey of Scotland.
         Scot. Stud. 12 : 187-89.

Kirby, R. P.
    1968 The ground moraines of Midlothian and East Lothian.
         Scott. J. Geol. 4 : 209-20.

Knox, P. and MacLaren, A.
    1978 Values and perceptions in descriptive approaches to
         urban-social geography.
         IN Herbert, D. T. and Johnston, R. J. (eds).
         Urban environment Vol. 1. London. Wiley.

Knox, P. and Pacione, M.
    1980 Locational behaviour, place preference and the inverse
         care law in the distribution of primary medical care.
         Geoforum 11 : 43-55.

Lea, K. J.
    1969 Hydro:electric generation in the Highlands of Scotland.
         Trans. Inst. Br. Geogr. 46 : 155-66.

Lea, K. J. (ed)
    1977 **A geography of Scotland.**
         Newton Abbot. David and Charles.

Lea, K. J., Gordon, G. and Bowler, I. R.
    1977 **A geography of Scotland.**
         Newton Abbot. David and Charles.

Learmonth, A. T. A.
    1950 The population of Skye. **S.G.M. 66** : 77-81.

         The floods of 12th. August, 1948, in south-east
         Scotland. **S.G.M. 66** : 147-152.

Lebon, J. H. G.
    1933 Development of the Ayrshire coal-field.
         S.G.M. 49 : 138-154.

1935 On watershed migration and the passes of the Lowther Hills. **S.G.M. 51** : 7-13.

1946 The face of the countryside in central Ayrshire during the eighteenth and nineteenth centuries. **S.G.M. 62** : 7-15.

The process of enclosure in the Eastern lowlands. **S.G.M. 62** : 100-110.

1952 Old maps and rural change in Ayrshire. **S.G.M. 68** : 104-9.

Ledger, D. C. et al.
1980 Rate of sedimentation in Kelly Reservoir, Strathclyde. **Scott. J. Geol. 16** : 281-5.

Lewis, F. J.
1906 The history of Scottish peat mosses and their relation to the Glacial period. **S.G.M. 22** : 241-52.

Lindsay, J.
1975 Charcoal iron smelting and its fuel supply ; the example of Lorn Furnace, Argyllshire, 1753-1876. **Jour. Hist. Geog. 1** : 283-98.

The history of oak coppice in Scotland. **Scottish Forestry 29** : 87-93.

Some aspects of timber supply in the Highlands 1700-1850. **Scot. Stud. 19** : 39-53.

1976 The commercial use of Highland woodland, 1750-1870. **S.G.M. 92** : 30-40.

1977 Forestry and agriculture in the Scottish Highlands, 1700-1850. **Ag. H. R. 25** : 23-36.

Linton, D. L.
1933 The origin of the Tweed drainage system. **S.G.M. 49** : 162-75.

1934 On the former connection between the Clyde and the Tweed. **S.G.M. 50** : 82-92.

1949 Watershed breaching by ice in Scotland. **Trans. Inst. Br. Geogr. 15** : 1-16.

Some Scottish river captures re-examined. **S.G.M. 65** : 123-32.

1951 Problems of Scottish scenery. **S.G.M. 67 : 65-85.**

Watershed breaching by ice in Scotland.
Trans. Inst. Br. Geogr. 15 : 1-15.

1968 Scenery as a natural resource. **S.G.M. 84 : 219-38.**

Linton, D. L. and Moisley, J. A.
1960 The origin of Loch Lomond. **S.G.M. 76 : 26-38.**

Lochhead, Elspeth
1981 Scotland as the cradle of modern academic geography in
Britain. **S.G.M. 97 : 98-109.**

1984 The Royal Scottish Geographical Society : the setting
and sources of its success. **S.G.M. 100 : 69-80.**

Lockhart, D. G.
1978 The planned villages of Aberdeenshire : the evidence
from newspaper advertisements. **S.G.M. 94 : 95-102.**

1979 The planned villages of Buchan, Aberdeenshire, 1750-
1900. **Trans. Buchan Field Club 18 : 40-51.**

1980 Scottish village plans : a preliminary analysis.
S.G.M. 96 : 141-57.

1981 Patterns of migration and movement of labour to the
planned villages of North-east Scotland.
S.G.M. 98 : 35-47.

Lowe, J. J., Gray, J. M., and Robinson, J.E. (eds)
1980 **Studies in the lateglacial of of northwest Europe.**
Oxford.

Lythe, S. G. E.
1938 The origin and development of Dundee - a study in
historical geography. **S.G.M. 54 : 344-58.**

McArthur, Margaret
1936 **Survey of Lochtayside 1769.** Edinburgh.

Macgregor, D. R.
1966 Social and economic effects of the Forth Road Bridge
with particular reference to the county of Fife.
S.G.M. 82 : 78-93.

McIntosh, I. G. and Marshall, C. B.
1966 **The face of Scotland.**

McNeil, J.
　　1973 The Fife coal industry, 1947-67. **S.G.M. 89** : 163-79.

MacPherson, A.
　　1964 Scotch whisky. **S.G.M. 80** : 99-106.

McSween, M. D.
　　1959 Transhumance in Skye. **S.G.M. 75** : 75-88.

Manley, G.
　　1945 Problems of Scottish climatology. **S.G.M. 61** : 73-76.

　　1957 Climatic fluctuations and fuel requirements.
　　S.G.M. 73 : 19-28.

Mather, A. S.
　　1971 Problems of afforestation in North Scotland.
　　Trans. Inst. Br. Geogr. 54 : 19-33.

Mathieson, J.
　　1924 General Wade and his military roads in the Highlands of
　　Scotland. **S.G.M. 40** : 193-212.

Mears, Frank (ed)
　　1948 **Regional plan for Central and South-east Scotland.**

Megaw, B. R. S.
　　1969 The date of Pont's survey and its background. **Scot.**
　　Stud. 13 : 71-74.

Mill, H. R.
　　1934 Flashlights on geography - featuring Scotland.
　　S.G.M. 50 : 193-209.

　　Recollections of the Society's early years.
　　S.G.M. 50 : 269-280.

Miller, Hugh
　　1857 **The testimony of the rocks.** Edinburgh. Constable.

Miller, R.
　　1956 Major General William Roy, FRS. **S.G.M. 72** : 97-100.

　　1967 Land use by summer shielings. **Scot. Stud. 11** : 193-219.

　　1976 **Orkney.** London.

Miller, R. and Tivy, Joy (eds)
　　1958 **The Glasgow region.** British Association, Glasgow.

Miller, R. and Watson, J. Wreford (eds)
1959 **Geographical essays in memory of Alan G. Ogilvie.**
Edinburgh.

Millman, R. N.
1974 **The making of the Scottish landscape.**

Moir, D. G.
1957 The roads of Scotland : statute labour roads.
S.G.M. 73 : 101-110, 167-175.

1973 **The early maps of Scotland.** 3rd. edition. vol 1.

1983 **The early maps of Scotland.** 3rd. edition, vol 2.

Moir, D. G. and Skelton, R. A.
1968 New light on the first Atlas of Scotland.
S.G.M. 84 : 149-59.

Moisley, H. A.
1960 Some Hebridean field systems. **Gwerin 3** : 22-35.

1961 North Uist in 1799. **S.G.M. 77** : 89-92.

1962 The Highlands and Islands : a crofting region?
Trans. Inst. Br. Geog. 31 : 83-97.

1966 The deserted Hebrides. **Scot. Stud. 10** : 44-68.

Moore, J. N.
1983 **The mapping of Scotland. A guide to the literature of Scottish cartography prior to the Ordnance Survey.**
O'Dell Memorial Monograph No. 15. Dept. of Geography, University of Aberdeen.

Morris, A. S.
1980 The nineteenth century Scottish carrier : patterns of decline trade. **S.G.M. 96** : 74-82.

Morrison, I. A.
1973 The Scottish lake dwelling survey.
Internat. Jour. Naut. Arch. 2.2 :

1974 **The North Sea Earls.** London. Gentry.

Mort, F. W.
1918 The rivers of south-west Scotland. **S.G.M. 34** : 361-8.

Mossman, R. C.
1895 Meteorology and health in Edinburgh.
Trans. R. Soc. Edinburgh. 38-40. (1895-1902).

Murray, J. and Pullar, L.
1908 **Bathymetric survey of the fresh water lochs of Scotland.** Edinburgh. (6 vols. 1908-1910).

National Library of Scotland
1984 **The map room and its services.** Edinburgh. National Library of Scotland.

Newbigin, M. I.
1901 **Life by the seashore.**

1905 The value of geography. **S.G.M. 21 : 1-4.**

1934 The Royal Scottish Geographical Society - the first fifty years. **S.G.M. 50 : 257-269.**

Newbigin, M. I. and Flett, J.
1918 **James Geikie - the man and the geologist.** Edinburgh.

Newey, W.
1966 Pollen analysis of sub-carse peats of the Forth valley. **Trans. Inst. Br. Geogr. 39 : 53-9.**

1967 Pollen analysis from south-east Scotland. **Bot. Soc. Edinb. 40 : 424-434.**

1970 Pollen analysis of Late-Weichselian deposits at Corstorphine, Edinburgh. **New Phytol. 69 : 1167-77.**

O'Dell, A. C.
1934 Lerwick - a port study. **S.G.M. 50 : 27-35.**

1939 **The historical geography of the Shetland Islands.** Lerwick.

1953 A view of Scotland in the middle of the eighteenth century. **S.G.M. 69 : 58-63.**

O'Dell, A. C. and Macintosh, J. (eds)
1963 **The north-east of Scotland.** British Association, Aberdeen.

O'Dell, A. C. and Walton, K.
1962 **The Highlands and Islands.** Edinburgh. Nelson.

O'Donoghue, Yolande
1977 **William Roy, 1726-1790.** London. British Library.

Ogilvie, Alan G.
1923 The physiography of the Moray Firth coast.
Trans. R. Soc. Edinburgh 53 : 377-404.

Ogilvie, Alan G. (ed)
1928 **Great Britain : essays in regional geography.**
Cambridge.

Osborne, R.
1958 The movements of people in Scotland, 1851-1951.
Scottish Studies 2 : 1-46.

Pacione, M.
1972 Traditional and new industries in Dundee.
S.G.M. 88 : 53-61.

1983 Neighbourhood communities in the modern city : some
evidence from Glasgow. **S.G.M. 99** : 169-81.

Pacione, M. & Gordon, George (eds)
1984 **Quality of life and human welfare.**
Norwich. Geobooks/R.S.G.S.

Parry, M.
1975 County maps as historical sources. A sequence of
surveys in southeast Scotland. **Scot. Stud. 19** : 15-26.

Secular climatic change and marginal agriculture.
Trans. Inst. Br. Geogr. 64 : 1-13.

1978 **Climatic change, agriculture and settlement.**
Folkestone.

Parry, M. L. and Slater, T. R. (eds)
1980 **The making of the Scottish countryside.**
London. Croom Helm.

Plant, J. A.
1966 **The climate of West Lothian.**
Met. Off., Clim. Serv. (Met. 0.3), Clim. Mem. 59.

1968 **The climate of Edinburgh.** (2nd. edtn.)
Met. Off., Clim. Serv. (Met. 0.3.), Clim. Mem. 54A.

Pocock, D. C. D.
1968 Shopping patterns in Dundee : some observations.
S.G.M. 84 : 108-117.

Price, Robert J.
1963 A glacial meltwater drainage system in Peebleshire,
Scotland. **S.G.M. 79** : 133-41.

1974 The glaciation of west central Scotland. A review.
S.G.M. 91 : 131-45.

1976 **Highland landforms.** Glasgow.

1983 **Scotland's environment during the last 30,000 years.**
Edinburgh. Scottish Academic Press.

Proudfoot, V. B. (ed)
1983 **Site, environment and economy.**
Assoc. Environmental Archaeologists, Symposium No. 7.
Oxford. British Archaeology Reports.

Rae, G. and Brown, C. E.
1966 **Geography of Scotland.**

Reid-Tait, E. S.
1930 Timothy Pont's map of Scotland. **S.G.M.** 46 : 210-4.

Rhymer, L.
1974 The Scottish kelp industry. **S.G.M.** 90 : 142-152.

Richards, A.
1969 Some aspects of the evolution of the coastline of
Northeast Skye. **S.G.M.** 85 : 122-31.

Ritchie, J.
1920 **The influence of man on animal life in Scotland.**
Cambridge.

Ritchie, W.
1966 The Post-glacial rise in sea-level and coastal changes
in the Uists. **Trans. Inst. Br. Geogr.** 39 : 79-87.

1967 The Machair of South Uist. **S.G.M.** 83 : 161-173.

1968 **The coastal morphology of North Uist.**
O'Dell Memorial Monographs No. 1,
Department of Geography, University of Aberdeen.

1972 The evolution of coastal sand dunes. **S.G.M.** 85 : 19-35.

Ritchie, W. and Mather, A.
1969 **The beaches of Sutherland.**
Department. of Geography, University of Aberdeen.

1970 **The beaches of Lewis and Harris.**
Department. of Geography, University of Aberdeen.

The beaches of Caithness.
Department of Geography, University of Aberdeen.

Robertson, C. J. (ed)
    1951 **Scientific survey of south-eastern Scotland.**
         British Association, Edinburgh.

    1955 The expansion of the arable area. **S.G.M. 72** : 1-20.

    1958 Locational and structural aspects of industry in
         Edinburgh. **S.G.M. 74** : 65-77.

    1964 New industries and New Towns in Scotland's industrial
         growth. **S.G.M. 80** : 114-123.

Robertson, D. J. (ed)
    1966 **Lothians regional survey and plan.** H.M.S.O.

Robinson, A. H. W.
    1958 The charting of the Scottish coasts.
         S.G.M. 74 : 116-127.

    1959 Two unrecorded manuscript charts by John Adair.
         S.G.M. 75 : 169-172.

Ross, W. C. A.
    1934 Highland emigration. **S.G.M. 50** : 155-65.

Scott, C. A.
    1915 The county of Renfrew. **S.G.M. 31** : 188-98 ; 225-40.

Scottish Office
    1968 **The Central Borders : a plan for expansion.** H.M.S.O.

Shakesby, R. A.
    1978 Dispersal of glacial erratics from Lennoxtown,
         Stirlingshire. **Scott. J. Geol. 14** : 81-86.

Shearer, J. E.
    1905 **Old maps and map makers of Scotland.** Stirling.

         The evolution of the map of Scotland.
         S.G.M. 21 : 289-301.

Sim, D.
    1982 **Change in the city centre.** London. Gower.

Sinclair, C. J.
    1977 Register House Plans (Collection of maps and plans held
         by the Scottish Record Office).
         Cartog. J. 14 : 140-141.

Sissons, J. B.
    1958 The deglaciation of part of East Lothian.
         Trans. Inst. Br. Geogr. 25 : 59-77.

         Some aspects of glacial drainage channels in Britain,
         part 1. **S.G.M. 76 : 131-46.**

    1961 Some aspects of glacial drainage channels in Brotain,
         part 2. **S.G.M. 77 : 15-36.**

    1962 A re-interpretation of the literature of the late-
         glacial shoreline in Scotland, with particular
         reference to the Forth area.
         Trans. Edin. Geol. Soc. 19 : 83.

    1964 The Perth readvance in Central Scotland.
         S.G.M. 79 : 151-63 (part 1) ; **80 :** 28-36 (part 2).

    1966 Relative sea-level changes between 10,300 and 8,300
         B.P. in part of the Carse of Stirling.
         Trans. Inst. Br. Geog. 39 : 19.

    1967 **The evolution of Scotland's scenery.**
         Edinburgh. Oliver and Boyd.

    1971 The geomorphology of Central Edinburgh.
         S.G.M. 87 : 185-96.

    1972 The last glaciers in part of the south-east Grampians.
         S.G.M. 88 : 168-81.

    1973 Delimiting the Loch Lomond Readvance in the eastern
         Grampians. **S.G.M. 89 : 138-9.**

    1976 A remarkable protalus rampart in Wester Ross.
         S.G.M. 92 : 182-90.

         Lateglacial marine erosion in south-east Scotland.
         S.G.M. 92 : 17-29.

    1979 The Loch Lomond Advance in the Cairngorm Mountains.
         S.G.M. 95 : 66-82.

Sissons, J. B. et al
    1965 Some pre-carse valleys in the Forth and Tay basins.
         S.G.M. 81 : 115.

    1966 Late-glacial and Post-glacial shorelines in south-east
         Scotland. **Trans. Inst. Br. Geog. 39 : 9-18.**

Skelton, R.
1967 The military survey of Scotland, 1747-1755.
S.G.M. 83 : 5-16.

Snodgrass, C. P.
1933 Stock farming and its relation to environment.
S.G.M. 49 : 24-34.

1943 Map of the economic regions of Scotland.
S.G.M. 59 : 15-18.

Soulsby, E. M.
1972 Changing sex ratios in the Scottish border counties.
S.G.M. 88 : 5-18.

Stanley, P. A., Farrington, J. H. and Mackenzie, R.
1981 Public transport in Easter Ross. H.I.D.B.

Steers, J. A.
1973 The coastline of Scotland.
Cambridge University Press.

Steven, H. M.
1951 The forests and forestry of Scotland.
S.G.M. 67 : 110-123.

Steven, T. M.
1911 A geographical description of the county of Ayr.
S.G.M. 28 : 281-90 ; 359-68.

Stewart, J.
1911 Notes on changes in the Highland district of Appin on
Tayside. S.G.M. 27 : 359-68 ; 381-90.

Stewart, J. Innes
1931 Scottish herring fishing industry.
S.G.M. 47 : 219-27, 286.

Stone, J. C.
1968 The evaluation of the Nidisdale manuscript map of
Timothy Pont. S.G.M. 84 : 160-71.

1970 The preparation of the Blaeu maps of Scotland : a
further assessment. S.G.M. 86 : 16-24.

1972 Origins and sources of the Blaeu atlas of Scotland with
particular reference to 'Extrima Scotia' (Atlas Novus,
1654). Imago Mundi 26 : 17-26.

Manuscript maps of north-east Scotland by Timpthy Pont.
Northern Scotland 1 : 143-50.

1973 The settlements of Nithsdale in the sixteenth century by Timothy Pont - a complete or partial record. **Trans. Dumfriesshire and Galloway Natural History and Archaeology Society 50** : 82-9.

1975 A copy of Mercator's **Scotia Regnum** with manuscript annotations. **Imago Mundi 27** : 43-46.

1979 A newly discovered map of Ettrick Forest, Scotland, by Robert Gordon of Straloch : implications for sources consulted by Joannis Blaeu. **Imago Mundi 31** : 84-87.

1983 Timothy Pont and the first topographic survey of Scotland circa 1583-1596 : an informative contemporary manuscript. **S.G.M. 99** : 161-8.

Storrie, M. C.
1961 A note on William Bald's plan of Ardnamurchan and Sunart. **Scot. Stud. 5** : 112.

1962 The Scottish whisky industry. **Trans. Inst. Br. Geogr. 31** : 97-114.

The census of Scotland as a source in the historical geography of Islay. **S.G.M. 78** : 152-165.

Two early resettlement schemes in Barra. **Scot. Stud. 6** : 71-84.

1965 Landholdings and settlement evolution in West Highland Scotland. **Geogr. Ann. 47B** : 138-61.

1969 William Bald, F.R.S.E., c. 1789-1857 ; surveyor, cartographer and civil engineer. **Trans. Inst. Br. Geogr. 47** : 205-231.

Sugden, D. E.
1968 The selectivity of glacial erosion in the Cairngorm Mountains. **Trans. Inst. Br. Geogr. 45** : 79-92.

1969 The age and form of corries in the Cairngorms. **S.G.M. 85** : 34-46.

1970 Landforms of deglaciation in the Cairngorm Mountains of Scotland. **Trans. Inst. Br. Geogr. 51** : 201-19.

Sutherland, D. G.
1980 Problems of radiocarbon dating deposits from newly
deglaciated terrain : examples from the Scottish
Lowlands.
IN Lowe, J.J. et al (eds)
Studies in the Lateglacial of northwest Europe.
Oxford.

Synge, F. M.
1956 The glaciation of north-east Scotland.
S.G.M. 72 : 129-143.

Thomas, M. F. & Coppock, J.T. (eds)
1980 **Land assessment in Scotland.**
Aberdeen University Press.

Third, Betty M. W.
1955 The changing landscape and social structure in the
Scottish lowlands as revealed by eighteenth century
estate plans. **S.G.M. 71** : 83-93.

1957 The significance of Scottish estate plans and
associated documents. **Scot. Stud. 1** : 39-64.

Timms, D. W. G. (ed)
1974 **The Stirling region.** Stirling University.

Tivy, Joy (ed)
1973 **The organic resources of Scotland : their nature and
evaluation.** Edinburgh. Oliver and Boyd.

Turner, W. H. K.
1952 The evolution of the pattern of the textile industry
within Dundee. **Trans. Inst. Br. Geogr. 18** : 107-119.

1953 Some eighteenth century developments in the textile
region of East Central Scotland. **S.G.M. 69** : 10-21.

1957 The textile industry of Dunfermline and Kirkcaldy 1700-
1900. **S.G.M. 73** : 129-145.

1958 The significance of water power in indistrial location
- some Perthshire examples. **S.G.M. 74** : 98-115.

1964 Wool textile manufacture in Scotland. **S.G.M. 80** : 81-9.

1966 The concentration of the jute and heavy linen
manufacturing industry in east-central Scotland.
S.G.M. 82 : 29-45.

1968 The growth of Dundee. **S.G.M. 84** : 76-89.

1972 Flax cultivation in Scotland, an historical geography. **Trans. Inst. Br. Geogr. 55** : 127-44.

1982 The development of flax-spinning mills in Scotland, 1787-1840. **S.G.M. 98** : 4-15.

The localisation of early spinning mills in the historic linen region of Scotland. **S.G.M. 98** : 77-86.

1983 Flax weaving in Scotland in the early nineteenth century. **S.G.M. 99** : 16-30.

Turnock, D.
1965 Hebridean car ferries. **Geography 50** : 375-8.

1965 Depopulation in north-east Scotland with reference to the countryside. **S.G.M. 84** : 256-68.

1967 Population studies and regional development in West Highland Britain. **Geogr. Ann. 49B** : 55-68.

Evolution of farming patterns in Lochaber. **Trans. Inst. Br. Geog 41** : 145-158.

Glenelg, Glengarry and Locheil : an evolutionary study of land use. **S.G.M. 83** : 89-103.

1969 North Morar : the improving movement on a West Highland estate. **S.G.M. 85** : 17-30.

1975 Small farms in north Scotland : an exploration in historical geography. **S.G.M. 91** : 164-181.

1977 Stages of agricultural improvement in the uplands of Scotland's Grampian region. **Jour. Hist. Geog. 3** : 327-347.

1979 Glenlivet - two centuries of rural planning in the Grampian uplands. **S.G.M. 95** : 165-181.

1983 **The historical geography of Scotland since 1707 : geographical aspects of modernisation.** Cambridge University Press.

Walton, K.
1956 Rattray ; a study in coastal evolution. **S.G.M. 72** : 85-96.

1961 Population changes in North-east Scotland 1696-1951. **Scottish Studies 5** : 149-180.

1963 The site of Aberdeen. **S.G.M. 79** : 79.

Wannop, A. R.
1964 Scottish agriculture. **S.G.M. 80** :

Warren, K.
1965 Locational problems of the Scottish iron and steel industry since 1760. **S.G.M. 81** : 18-36 and 87-103.

Watson, J. A. Scott
1932 The rise and development of the sheep industry in the Highlands and North Scotland. **Trans. Highld. Agric. Soc. Scot. (5th series) 44** : 1-25.

Watson, J. Wreford
1939 Forest or bog : man the deciding factor. **S.G.M. 55** : 148-61.

Watson, J. Wreford (ed)
1966 **Atlas of Edinburgh.** Geographical Association.

Welch, R. V.
1970 Immigrant manufacturing industry established in Scotland between 1945 and 1968 : some structural and locational characteristics. **S.G.M. 86** : 134-148.

1974 Manufacturing change on Greater Clydeside in the 1950s and 1960s. **S.G.M. 90** : 168-178.

Whitehand, J. W. R.
1972 Building cycles and the spatial pattern of urban growth. **Trans. Inst. Br. Geogr. NS2** : 400-416.

1978 Long term changes in the form of the city centre : the case for redevelopment. **Geogr. Ann. 60B** : 79-86.

Whittington, G.
1974 The regionalism of Lewis Grassic Gibbon. **S.G.M. 90** : 75-84.

Whittington, G. and
1977 Planning and growth in the medieval Scottish burgh : the example of St. Andrews. **Trans. Inst. Br. Geogr. NS2** : 279-95.

Whittington, G. and Whyte, I. D. (eds)
1983 **An historical geography of Scotland.** London. Academic Press.

Whyte, I. D.
    1976 **Scottish historical geography : survey and prospect.**
         Discussion Paper No. 8, Department of Geography,
         Edinburgh University.

    1978 Scottish historical geography - a review.
         S.G.M. 94 : 4-23.

    1979 The growth of periodic market centres in Scotland,
         1600-1707. **S.G.M. 95 : 13-26.**

    1981 The evolution of rural settlement in Lowland Scotland
         in medieval and early modern times : an exploration.
         S.G.M. 97 : 4-15.

Wilson, G.
    1980 Industrial coal markets in Fife, 1760-1860.
         S.G.M. 96 : 83-90.

Withers, C. W. J.
    1984 'The image of the land' : Scotland's geography through
         her language and literature. **S.G.M. 100 : 81-95.**

Wood, J. D.
    1964 Scottish migration overseas. **S.G.M. 80 : 164-76.**

Woolmer, H.
    1970 Granton-on Spey : an eighteenth century new town.
         Town Plan. Rev. 41 : 237-49.

AUTHORS

Ian H. Adams is both a graduate and a Senior Lecturer in Geography of Edinburgh University. He is a consultant at the Scottish Record Office and the author of several books on the historical geography of Scotland including **The making of urban Scotland, Peter May - Land Surveyor, 1749-1793** and **Agrarian landscape terms.**

A. J. Crosbie, a graduate of Aberdeen and Edinburgh Universities, is Head of the Department of Geography at the University of Edinburgh and a member of the Council of the Royal Scottish Geographical Society. He has worked extensively in the tropics in West Africa, Central America and,particularly, in South and Southeast Asia. Currently, he is contributing to a new publication on **Geographical perspectives on development in Southeast Asia** and is writing a book on **The Pacific Rim.** From 1966 to 1970 he directed the Air Pollution Unit at Edinburgh University and for the past five years has been engaged on contract research on the application of geographical information systems and computer mapping to Scottish problems.

George Gordon, a graduate of Edinburgh University, is Senior Lecturer in Geography and Dean of the Faculty of Arts and Social Studies in the University of Strathclyde. He is co-editor of books on **Scotish urban history** and **Quality of life and human welfare,** editor of **Perspectives of the Scottish City** (in press) and contributed to **A geography of Scotland, An historical geography of Scotland,** and **The Stirling region.**